FICTION

Contents

PAGE 134

PAGE 142

PAGE 164

FEATURE

FANCY THAT!

PANCAKES PLEASE

PUZZLES

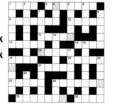

DC Thomson While every reasonable care will be taken, neither D C Thomson & Co, Ltd,
nor its agents accept liability for loss or damage to any material submitted
to this publication.

Strictly Sparkling

Prima ballerina Darcey Bussell, the kindest of the TV show's judges, explains her lifelong love of dance

The wonderful thing about *Strictly* is that it sends such a positive message about dance. I believe in how dance lifts you and makes you feel. Dance and music wake up every sense and make you feel good about life," Darcey declares.

The ballet superstar has been making us feel good about dance long before she joined the *Strictly* judges.

"I went to ballet school when I was five, although I think my mother would have loved to send me earlier, just to burn off some energy!

always wanting to make people smile. I wanted them to watch me constantly."

Her dancing career took off once she became principal dancer for the Royal Ballet at the tender age of 20 in 1989. She has performed more than 80 roles in ballets around the world.

One of her most memorable moments was a guest performance for New York City Ballet, aged 22. "I received a standing ovation – that was an incredible moment."

More standing ovations have followed, especially when she joined the judging panel of *Strictly*.

"As a child, I was very attention-seeking. I wanted people to watch me constantly"

"As a child, I was horribly energetic. I didn't sit down for two seconds, and was always told to keep still but I found it hard.

"I was also a bit of a show-off, always wanting to perform for everyone, and wanting to wear fancy dress – which I think is pretty normal, as I have two daughters and they were exactly the same when they were young.

"I was very attention-seeking, I was

"I probably take *Strictly* more seriously than the average person because I understand it. You do just get totally over the moon when you see someone enjoying something you love.

"They might not be able to get the technique by tomorrow, but it doesn't matter. They're so testing themselves and you have to admire that."

Continued overleaf

Strictly Speaking

Some candid quotes from the well-loved regulars...

Fab-u-lous!

"When I did *Celebrity Masterchef* I wasn't nervous until they said, "Your time starts now." Then I went to pieces, so I can completely understand why people do the same on *Strictly*. I do feel for them – but sadly, they need to get through it and be fab-ul-ous!"
Judge Craig Revel Horwood

Take To The Floor

"In the last moments before I take to the dance floor I feel very nervous, but I'm also worrying about my partner and how they are going to cope. Sometimes I'm thinking 'Oh God, what have I done?' – but it's a lovely place to find myself." *Strictly veteran Anton du Beke*
Continued overleaf

We're Mates!

"You can't fake it on live TV – it's the most honest form of television there is. It's a real friendship and I think the public can see that." *Tess Daly*

"The viewers can spot it if you get on. Fakery and nonsense can be seen from a mile off." *Claudia Winkleman*

Strictly Behind The Scenes

Sneak a glimpse of the frantic activity behind the glitz!

Before the show, the audience is in place for at least an hour in advance of the opening credits rolling. They are entertained by warm-up guy Stuart Holdham while production staff prepare the show.

Certain sections of the weekend shows are pre-recorded, such as some professional dance numbers, the guest singer's slot and some of the presenter's links to camera. So the pros have already been working really hard by the time they escort their celebrities down those glittery steps!

Sixteen couples, four judges and two presenters have to be readied for the show, and additional styling is required for the recording of the results show later that evening. The female professionals have five or six different looks, per show! The ladies can take more than two hours to prepare; the hair and make-up team start at 9am to apply endless rounds of lashes, curlers, make-up and body shimmer and to deal with issues such as masking bruises.

The dancers will also have post-rehearsal top-ups during the day to ensure they remain camera-ready for the evening's show.

The band pull off a small miracle every week

A lot of effort goes into those posh frocks!

A whopping ten litres of spray tan is used during the series, administered on a Friday, around the demands of the studio rehearsal.

Each dress is designed according to the physical attributes of its wearer and the individual style of each dance, and created from fabric that best suits the requirements of the choreography.

Costume designer Vicky Gill also ensures that there is plenty of variety in style and colour across all the contestants. Sometimes, after Saturday's dress rehearsal, adjustments are still being made right up to the start of the live show.

Dresses are designed around a leotard base, so they fit securely and embarrassing costume malfunctions are avoided. The men's shirts are also designed in a leotard style, so they don't become untucked. Even the skimpiest of frocks still have a mic pack hidden – often in the cup of the bust – so the couples can talk after their performance. Dance shoes are deliberately rather plain and inconspicuous. None of the dancers want attention to be drawn to their feet!

Strictly's producers work with the professional dancers to select music suiting the style and tempo of each dance. Not all the dancers' choices are approved – the music director needs to ensure a wide variety of music in each show.

It takes up to four hours to arrange each number for the in-house band to perform. They manage an incredible feat each week, performing multiple songs live, with very little rehearsal and often not seeing their scores until the day of the show!

And a last word from Len?

"I always think of a show like a plant – a little pruning now and then keeps it healthy!"

Sue Moorcroft

Sharing Carrie

Meeting his daughter had been a huge shock for Tom. Would he run away again – or step up this time?

B ah-bye," cooed Carrie, waving. Cuddling the little girl to her heart, Hannah watched from the doorstep as Tom fumbled dazedly with his car keys.

She supposed it wasn't every day he dropped in on an old girlfriend and found her bringing up a child – *his* child. Not surprising he couldn't get away quickly enough. Just disappointing.

"Gog?" Carrie pointed as Tom's car kangarooed away from the kerb.

Hannah closed the door.

"Not a dog. A man, driving his car."

"Car," Carrie agreed, grinning a nose-wrinkled, three-tooth grin.

Hannah grinned back. Carrie was heart-stopping, Carrie made everything worthwhile. Carrie had taken Hannah's life, turned it upside-down and shaken it like a snow-scene.

Tonight, instead of piling on the Saturday evening glam as she had in the years BC – Before Carrie – Hannah was preparing for Carrie's bath routine of bubbles and giggles, before bedtime stories, then another evening alone with *Strictly* and a glass of wine.

Two years BC, Hannah had spent Saturday evenings with Tom, and it had been movies or clubs and laughter. Then Tom, suddenly restless, had told Hannah he wasn't ready to settle down.

"I haven't asked you to," she pointed out, bewildered.

Tom fidgeted. "I know you haven't. But all your friends are getting married and you seem so into it. I feel as if you think we're next, but I haven't done everything I want to do before getting tied down."

Hannah's heart shrivelled, not least because she had been entertaining daydreams of wedding days and Happy Ever After. Now it seemed that letting her feelings show had driven Tom away.

Yet the state of her heart didn't matter; she wasn't about to "tie down" the man she loved. She forced a smile.

"Don't let me hold you back. Enjoy your new life."

Tom had looked shaken.

"Do you mean…? Is this… it, then?"

Turning away before he saw her tears, Hannah had shrugged. "Sounds like it."

Twenty-two months ago, Tom had left for a new life in London.

Hannah had hardly had time to hope

Continued overleaf

Continued from previous page

he'd be happy before finding herself plunged into her own new life of shock and adjustment, of howling anxiety followed by overwhelming love, of nappies, exhaustion and no time off.

And whenever she thought of her daughter's father it was in the past tense – so it had been a jolt to find him at her door today, smiling the smile that stopped her breath. "I'm back in the area and thought I'd see how you … aahhh!" Or maybe it was, "Arghhhh!" as Carrie tottered into view and Tom's smile froze.

Hannah sighed. "You'd better come in." She drew Tom gently through the door and sat him down like a trauma victim with a cup of hot tea.

"Why did you keep her a secret?"

Hannah folded her arms. "I didn't know until you'd gone. And who was I supposed to tell? Your empty house?"

"My old firm had my new address."

"But I didn't."

"You could have –"

"Tied you down?"

"That's not fair!"

They exchanged opposing views in quiet voices while Carrie blithely demonstrated her talent for staggering around the furniture. Then she pulled off one ribbon-bowed sock and made a present of it to Tom.

"Got to go," he gulped. "Got to get my head round this." Which was how Hannah and Carrie had come to watch him leave.

"Can we talk?" He returned the next day, dark hair fluttering in the breeze, eyes brown in the morning light.

Hannah groaned and let him wait while she showered and dressed them both, choosing for Carrie her favourite dress and the ribbed tights that made her legs look like two fat sticks of liquorice. When she reappeared, he'd boiled the kettle, scenting the air with instant coffee, and settled on a kitchen chair.

From Hannah's arms, Carrie pointed at him and shouted, "Ha!"

He pointed back, beaming.

"Ha to you, too!"

Carrie hooted and Tom laughed and Hannah realised that things were about to change again. The knowledge was in Tom's eyes as he gazed at his daughter and held out his arms.

Over Carrie's head, Tom smiled tentatively. "I want to be in her life, not just financially – that goes without saying. I want her to have both parents, and it's perfectly possible now I've moved back. How on earth have you managed, alone?"

"The sudden onset of efficiency." Hannah flippantly minimised the racing from job to child-minder to home, the forward planning of meals and shopping, the exhausted evenings after Carrie was in bed. "What made you move back?"

Vaguely, Tom shrugged, tickling Carrie until she gurgled with joy.

Tom began to call to play with Carrie and take her out in her navy-chequered buggy with the big wheels. They'd report to Hannah the progress of the ducks in the park and how high the new swing swung.

Hannah taught him how to change a nappy, a daunting task now that Carrie was convinced the idea was to flip over and scamper off like a puppy.

The time came when Tom felt sufficiently well trained to cope with Carrie for a whole day, and, as she helped him transfer the child seat from her car to his, Hannah observed, nonchalantly, "You never said why you moved back."

Tom looked vague again.

"Oh, you know. London. Too many people, not enough friends."

She posted Carrie into her car seat, was free, and that was a relief because life had been hard work alone. It began to seem fair and natural to involve Tom in decisions about Carrie or to give him the opportunity to clap when Carrie learned something marvellous.

Then, one day, he arrived armed with a new idea.

"Remember I said I wanted her to have both parents? Sometimes that means both at once. I want us to go out as a family."

Hannah's stomach did a flip. "Everything's fine as it is. Why change it?"

"I want what's best for Carrie. It's not natural for one of us to pass her to the other before rushing off. She must feel like a relay baton."

Hannah grumbled, "I suppose it'll be OK," to hide the fact that it sounded more than OK. Sternly, she told her heart not to

"It's not natural for us to hand her over and dash off. She must feel like a relay baton"

feeling a tiny tug of regret that Carrie, faithlessly, seemed to have accepted her father as if he'd always been there – as if the time Hannah had cared for her alone counted for nothing.

Tom checked Carrie's straps.

"I'll have her back by six."

Assailed by last minute jitters, Hannah hopped about on the pavement yelling through the car window. "Have you got enough nappies? And my phone number?"

But he was fine with Carrie, of course. They returned on schedule, Carrie beaming – four teeth now – holding her arms out to Hannah.

Tom began to take Carrie out regularly or to babysit in the evenings so Hannah

read anything into this new development. Tom wanted what was best for Carrie, and so did Hannah.

He beamed. "Let's give Carrie her first taste of the seaside."

"But it's winter!"

"Then the beach won't be crowded."

They bundled into Tom's car and drove to the coast. On the prom, the salty wind upended their hair, whipping roses into their cheeks and smiles onto their lips.

Their daughter toddled between them staring at the glassy green waves that danced in the winter sun and broke in froth on the beach, gulls wheeling and waltzing on the wind. She ate a doughnut **Continued overleaf**

Continued from previous page

and gazed at the sugar crystals it left on her fingers. "Bun! More, please." She sat in a turquoise teacup with a yellow saucer on the almost deserted toddlers' merry-go-round and shook with giggles. As the ride went on she quietened, and fell asleep.

"Carrie." Despair broke his voice.

Hannah withdrew her hands into her sleeves, away from the chill breeze.

"We give her everything she needs."

He snapped the buggy brake on, making Carrie stir.

"Everything except a family. We've

"We didn't want the same things." The admission made her vision blur with tears

Tom scooped her gently out of the teacup and into her buggy. Hannah tucked a blanket around her before they moved on to climb the steep path to the cliff top where the music of the merry-go-round was replaced by the whipping of the wind.

Hannah paused to thread herself into her fleece jacket. Tom held it so she could find the sleeve. She looked up and found him looking unusually intent.

Suddenly he burst into words as if scared he'd lose his nerve.

"Do you think there's any chance for us, if we try again? Will you try again?"

Slowly, she zipped up her fleece, her lower lip trying not to tremble as her pain came flooding back. "Why?"

ended up as friends who share a daughter. Life's about love and togetherness, not parenting by committee."

His hands grasped Hannah's, then slackened and dropped when she didn't wind her fingers around his. His face fell.

"We could have been together when Carrie was coming. This is my fault."

"But we didn't want the same things." The admission made her vision blur as a tear tipped onto her cheek.

He tried to slip his arms around her but Hannah pulled away.

"It's not enough, just to share Carrie."

He took a step back. "You're right." And he turned and began to run.

Shaken, she watched him, through the

gate on the cliff-top, down the zig-zag pathway, smaller and smaller, down the stairs at the bottom and onto the sand, packed hard, smoothed by the receding tide. From above he looked like a cartoon, bobbling along the high-tide mark until he found a big shard of driftwood.

He looked up, waved, then began to write in the wet sand with the wood.

She leaned over the guardrail, holding her hair back from her eyes. Other people had stopped, up and down the path, to watch, too, as the letters began to form *I LOVE YOU HANNAH!*

Hannah's heart started to thunder as she watched Tom race back up the stairs, up the zig-zag path, bigger and bigger, ignoring the grins of bystanders, until he panted, life-sized, at her side.

"It's not only Carrie. You're the reason I didn't settle in London. I missed you."

He grabbed her hands again, eyes fixed pleadingly on hers.

"I was immature. I didn't realise that life with you wouldn't be tying myself down – it would be love and security. You were the most important thing in my life and all the freedom in the world meant nothing compared with losing you. Do you… do you still have feelings for me?"

Hannah examined her heart, which was quivering uncertainly at the prospect that Tom might mean it. "Ye-es…"

"Then…?" His gaze never wavered.

Behind them, Carrie stirred. She sat up and called, "Bun, please!"

"Just a minute, sweetie." Tom gripped Hannah's hands so she couldn't pull away. "This is even more important than a bun."

Hannah examined the face of her daughter's father. She imagined how it would be to share more than Carrie – to share their lives. She glanced back down at where *I LOVE YOU, HANNAH!* was written in the sand for everyone to see.

"OK. Let's try. But you may be underestimating the importance of a bun."

Tom laughed, pulling her against him, eyes sparkling in the winter sun.

"I think it's traditional to seal these moments with a kiss –"

Carrie began to chant, "Bun! Bun! BUN! More, please!"

He sighed. "But I suppose it can come after the bun."

Hannah felt glad laughter bubbling up inside. "Welcome to family life!"

Turn over to find out more about best-selling author Sue Moorcroft.

A Moment With Sue

...is likely to involve wine, chocolate and an early start

What inspires you to write?

It's more of a compulsion than an inspiration. Although it's not always easy to create a satisfying story with characters to care about and conflicts I'd like to shine a light on, my plotty little mind thrives on it. And, pragmatically, what a fantastic way to earn a living!

When are you happiest?

Enjoying the company of family or friends. If a chocolate dessert and a glass of cold white wine is involved, so much the better.

What is your favourite novel?

A Town Like Alice by Nevil Shute. It was the first "grown up" novel I read, when I was about nine. My dad was a Nevil Shute fan and between us we collected all his books. We lost Dad a long time ago but I have our joint collection on a shelf in front of me as I type this page.

How do you manage your time?

I'm quite disciplined. Although my job can be flexible when I wish it to be or it needs to be, I build it on my own version of office hours. I'm usually at my desk by 7.15am with a cuppa and an hour later I eat my breakfast, also at my desk.

Do you ever get a bee in your bonnet?

Oh my goodness, yes! And I have an enormous bonnet. Two of the biggest, buzziest bees are called Injustice and Inequality.

What is your latest novel about?

Just for the Holidays features Leah Beaumont, who has carefully avoided having a husband and children, finding herself trapped in France looking after her sister's husband and children. She's glad of the support of the single dad next door – until his ex-wife turns up...

Find out more about Sue's latest novel and past work on www.suemoorcroft.com **or connect with her on social media:**
Twitter: @suemoorcroft **Facebook:** facebook.com/SueMoorcroftAuthor **and** sue.moorcroft.3
Instagram: SueMoorcroftAuthor

Sue Moorcroft

Brain BOOSTERS

Codeword

Each letter of the alphabet has been replaced by a number. The numbers for the first name of our pictured celebrity are given.

Helen Mirren is one of only 21 people to have achieved which accolade?

6		11		19		9 **H**		25		19		7
11	8	22	4	19	25	21	4		21	4	19	23	15	5
	23		3		7		21 **L**		18		23		26
19	6	3	7	8	5		4 **E**	12	25	18	26	8	4	26
	7		4				15 **N**		11		2		23
8	12	16	21	10					20	19	22	4	26
	15			4						23		12
17	19	8	20	11				11	14	8	16	11
	2		21					18		21
2	8	6	19	23				25	7	24	18	12
	13		16		20		11		15		10
12	19	23	1	18	23	19	12	16	11	19	21	12	11
	5		19		19		4		7		25		4
5	18	7	6	9	10		21	8	20	4	21	18	15	13
	23		14		11		21		20		4		5

A B C D É F G Ĥ I J K Ł M Ń O P Q R S T U V W X Y Z

| 1 | 2 | 3 | 4 **E** | 5 | 6 | 7 | 8 | 9 **H** | 10 | 11 | 12 | 13 |
| 14 | 15 **N** | 16 | 17 | 18 | 19 | 20 | 21 **L** | 22 | 23 | 24 | 25 | 26 |

| 5 | 23 | 8 | 16 | 21 **L** | 4 **E** | | 6 | 23 | 18 | 17 | 15 **N** | | 18 | 20 | | 19 | 6 | 5 | 8 | 15 **N** | 13 |

Stand-In Santa

What will it take for stressed and lonely Moira to succumb to the magic of the festive season?

By Lydia Jones

W hat do you mean, he's not taking the job?"

I stare at my assistant in horror.

"He said his premium bonds had come up." Amy squirms. "So he's going away for Christmas. To – um – Jamaica."

Poor Amy is puce in the face; she looks about ready to bolt. It makes me realise how hard I have been on her these last few stressful weeks.

"Right." I grab bag and coat. "I can't deal with this now. I'm off out for lunch."

"But Moira, you never take lunch."

"I do today."

Wind buffets bare tree branches in the park; I pull up my coat collar and wish I'd worn something as sensible as a scarf.

No Santa Claus.

After all the supply problems and product cancellations; now Dalrymple's Department Store has no Santa Claus this Christmas.

I'm section head of Toys.

This Christmas was supposed to be my platform to prove my worth; pave my way for promotion.

Since Mr Dalrymple sold out to a national chain in spring, all senior staff have been under close scrutiny from Mr Stephens, the new store manager. He says we're a team but Mr Smarmy Stephens isn't fooling anybody: there will be some serious "restructuring" for any manager not succeeding this festive season.

I'm young for a section head; I don't have a degree in retail management. Mr Dalrymple believed in me but Mr Stephens is unconvinced. For me, this Christmas is less about good tidings of joy and more about good takings for toys.

Next Saturday is the Christmas lights switch-on – market stalls; dancers; bands; fireworks. Dalrymple's Santa is star of the parade. Just shoot me now.

I press fingers into my eye sockets and murmur a prayer for a miracle.

I love this job. I don't want to watch some whizzkid from head office waltz in to take charge. "Toys" is mine. I take a gulp of icy air; tilt my chin. And I am not giving it up without a fight. Even if I have to wear the Santa suit myself.

"Applicant for the job of Santa," Amy says when I stride back onto the shop-floor. She beckons.

Continued overleaf

In the waiting area I see a distinguished looking man sporting a significant salt and pepper beard.

"How on earth?"

"Search me," Amy says. "He said he'd heard there was a vacancy. This is his CV."

"His name is Mr Noel."

"You're kidding."

"He's lovely," she mouths as I push open the door.

"Hello Mr – err – Noel."

"Nicholas."

He stands, in an endearingly old-fashioned gesture, and extends a hand.

"Your name is Nicholas?"

This is so a set-up. I bet it's that you've ever seen in a film. He's well-rehearsed. I'm impressed my rivals managed to rustle him up so quickly.

To buy some time, I scan his CV. Previous work; up-to-date child protection certificate.

"You're very experienced – err – Nicholas. How come you're not already contracted this Christmas?"

"My wife and I agreed I'd give the store work a miss this year. But I heard you were stuck."

"Ah, yes. How did you hear? About the – um – vacancy?" I bristle.

"Dan Carter told me."

"Dan?"

Why can't I even mention his name

Somehow I feel as if his guileless blue eyes can see right into my internal chaos

supercilious Sophie from cosmetics. As Mr Stephens' niece she's supposed to be working her way up but she acts like it's already her store.

My skin prickles; I glance anxiously sideways to spot sniggering conspirators but there are none.

I sit; so does he.

"Nicholas is your real name, right?"

He looks like he doesn't understand the question. I wonder at what point he's going to come clean and admit that he's really a stooge.

"I mean, you're not going to get into any street fights and end up in court?"

Now he looks alarmed.

"Like in the movie," I explain. "You know – *Miracle on 34th Street*?"

"Oh, no – yes – ha, ha, ho – no."

He even laughs like every "real" Santa without a million winged fiends taking flight inside my chest?

"How do you know D – our head of Electricals?" I try to brazen it out.

"I'm a sort of – family friend."

His blue eyes are guileless but somehow I feel as if he can see right into my internal chaos.

Dan Carter: please let him not be in cahoots with horrible Sophie Stephens in this set-up. Surely he's not so desperate to hold onto his job?

I regard Nicholas Noel silently for a second, trying to decide whether this really is a set-up or actually just an amazing stroke of luck.

An email alert pops up on my PC from Mr Stephens. Its title is *Santa replacement?*

"OK." I exhale. "You've got the job."

If it does turn out to be a joke, it will just have to be on me for now.

"You'd better go to HR and have a fitting for the suit," I tell him.

"I have my own suit."

"Of course you do."

I shake my head in disbelief.

I heard you already got a new Santa," Dan says later as we both step into the lift. "Well done."

"Yeah." I squash into a space between other bodies. "Thanks for that."

"So –" he makes an awkward nodding gesture. "Toys going well?"

"Oh, you know… Electricals?"

I'm acutely aware of everyone in the lift; embarrassed that my feelings for Dan must be so obvious, I might as well be wearing a flashing sign.

If I am, it seems it's one he can't read. Or maybe he doesn't want to.

"Just had a few supply problems."

"Ah." I nod in sympathy. Supply problems I know all about.

The lift reaches the subterranean store car park; everyone shuffles forward.

"Night then, Moira."

"Night, Dan."

We are, you see, the original *Love, Actually* office couple. You remember the ones – all that awkward nodding, smiling and staring.

Dan joined Dalrymple's just after me and ever since I've been besotted. If I were a teenager I'd be doodling his name on pieces of paper with hearts drawn round it. For a supposed sophisticated career woman I am pathetic. But I can't quite seem to get a grip.

We speak a bit, and smile. But nothing ever happens.

"You want your heads banging together," my sister says.

"Maybe he just doesn't fancy me."

Nicholas Noel is awesome. Even children terrified by the whole meeting-Santa-situation come away from him smiling.

I have to admit he's done his homework.

"That's the magic of Pepper Minstix, you see," I overhear him saying to a child curious about the famous workshop's location. "He's my Head of Security elf. It's his job to keep our workshop secret; his spells mean no one ever sees us."

Over the next few weeks I see my sales figures soar; even Mr Stephens deigns to come down to Toys and compliment me.

Part of me still wonders whether this will all blow up in my face but as weeks pass without Nicholas proving to be any problem I start to believe I just got lucky. Maybe this huge hike in my profits is reward for all those years of hard work.

I feel stress melting like snow; I smile more; I'm even chatty with Dan.

"Nicholas is a great find," Dan says on our nightly lift descent together. "I brought my cousin to see him – he's a pretty streetwise little character, even at six and a half, but Nicholas had him believing.

Continued overleaf

They had this really detailed discussion about which reindeer work the hardest."

"Really?" I'm smiling like an idiot.

"It's Vixen and Prancer apparently." Dan grins. "Rudolph is rubbish."

I giggle.

"We've reached the car park. People start to file off towards cars; Dan and I linger by the lift.

"Err –" He jingles car keys. "I was actually going to do a bit of shopping myself. I like to get stuff we don't sell – shows more thought, somehow. I might grab something to eat too. I don't suppose – you'd like to come? I could do with some help ticking off the sister and mother boxes of my Christmas list."

Before the urgent "yes" is out of my mouth, I remember.

"Oh – sorry, I can't. I'm babysitting for my niece tonight."

He looks as if I've just slapped him.

"Of course – no problem at all if you're busy. It was just a thought – but

"Tell me about it," I grunt.

"You'll have to ask him out."

"Rhona – you're shameless!"

"I know." She giggles. "Must be the prospect of a night out with my wonderful husband courtesy of the best sister a girl could get."

"Keep flattering – I deserve it. That and chocolate cake."

"In the kitchen." She grins. "Popcorn too. I've left a list of approved films you can watch with Emily."

"Seriously," she says as she tugs on her coat. "It's a Christmas tradition. Manoeuvre that man under some mistletoe pronto."

"Don't talk to me about tradition. My Christmas is about money – parents spending it and me persuading them to spend it with me."

I don't want to watch a DVD," Emily announces as I sink onto the sofa with a bowl of popcorn. "There's a new Christmas movie on TV."

"It's a Christmas tradition. Manoeuvre that man under some mistletoe pronto"

naturally you wouldn't – it's OK, Moira."

He's backing away. I want to say something to stop him: to make him see I'm not just fobbing him off. But the words won't come.

"Night, Moira."

"Night, Dan."

Moira, I'm so sorry," my sister says when I tell her. "How long has this been going on? And then you can't go because of me."

"But your mum said to me –"

Emily rolls eyes in an expression so like my sister I have to smile.

"It's only because the TV movie shows that Santa is a man in a suit. Mum thinks I still believe in all that."

"Don't you?"

"Nah, but it doesn't matter."

"Doesn't it?"

"Aunty Moira –" My eight-year-old niece shoots me a withering look. "It's the magic that matters. Santa is a made-up story to remind people that happy things happen when we're kind to each other."

"Gosh, Emily – that's deep."

"It's obvious really." She speaks as if to a dense toddler. "At Christmas most people try to do nice things for friends and family, don't they? Even for strangers sometimes."

"I suppose."

"That's the magic of Christmas." She shrugs.

"So you won't be writing a Santa present list, then?"

"Don't be silly, Aunty Moira."

She giggles; so do I.

This conversation stays with me so that when I return to the store I find I see the frantic present buying less in terms of my department's sales figures and more as evidence of forgotten Christmas spirit.

"You've done an amazing job," I say to Nicholas on Christmas Eve. "Made my Christmas. Thank you."

"Christmas is for being with the people you love, Moira." He winks one of those intense blue eyes at me. "It's the magic that matters."

Emily's words.

"But on the subject of work –" He withdraws an envelope from his jacket. "I almost forgot. Mr Stephens gave me your final sales report to pass on."

"Thanks." I don't know why but it no longer matters so much. "Happy Christmas, Nicholas."

"Happy Christmas, Moira."

However the sales figures aren't mine. The report shows healthy sales for Electricals; Dan will be eager for this.

I scan the store in vain; finally I pocket the envelope and head for the lift.

"I was looking for you," he says as I approach. "I seem to have your sales report. I opened it – sorry. But well done."

"Me too." I shake my head. "I mean, I've got yours. Nicholas gave it to me."

"And me."

"Odd. I thought he said he was a family friend."

"Of yours – yes."

"No – of yours."

It takes a few seconds for us to take this information in.

In the pause the lift pings; doors open. Miraculously it is empty. Over the sprinkler on the ceiling, someone has hung a huge bunch of mistletoe.

As we step inside, Dan looks up; so do I.

"Seems a pity to waste that."

He smiles slowly.

"Yes – it does."

I allow myself to be pulled into Dan's arms at long last.

It must be my imagination but as the lift doors slide together and Dan's lips meet mine, I swear I hear a laugh that sounds exactly like Santa.

• •

THE AUTHOR SAYS...

"Christmas shopping can be so stressful – and just as bad for store staff. Inspired by favourite festive movies, I wanted to give one stressed-out worker a happy Christmas."

Pots And Pickles

Josie was determined to carry on with her stall, even without her husband – but the vicar had other ideas

By Jean Cullop

The new vicar was causing quite a stir. Reverend Gracie was fizzing with innovative ideas for St Mark's Christmas Bazaar. Not everyone had approved.

Josie Watts was helping prepare the tombola. It was a job she usually enjoyed – but this year Josie would be relieved when today was over.

She had always contributed pickles and jams. Her husband Colin threw pots, each pastel design reflecting his gentle personality. Together they were Pots and Pickles. But after fifty years together, Colin quietly passed away with the soft spring breeze leaving an incredible void.

How she missed him! How she longed to hear him snoring, or to have cause to grumble when he messed up her kitchen!

The seasonably coloured bazaar buzzed excitedly as folk put the finishing touches to their stalls. Josie's produce was being displayed by Mary Dickens – but not how Josie would have displayed them.

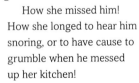

Why did things have to change? Why couldn't it all be just the same as it had been last year, when Colin had been by her side?

A few weeks ago, Reverend Gracie asked to speak with Josie after morning service. The young vicar was beaming with enthusiasm.

"Mrs Watts, I have some new ideas for the bazaar. I hope you can help me."

Gracie's ideas tended to incur a great deal of work. Josie was cautious.

The vicar continued, "I understand you provide a stall called Pots and Pickles?"

"Just pickles this year, Vicar," Josie replied sadly. "My husband Colin did the pots but he's no longer here."

"I know, my dear… and do please call me Gracie… I wonder whether this year you would like to help with another area."

"But Pots and Pickles is always popular and I've plenty of pickles, not to mention jams." Unsettled, Josie busied herself cleaning the coffee tables but the vicar trailed behind her like a persistent puppy.

"We are doing new stalls this year," she explained. "One will be toys with a Christmas theme. We need an experienced helper and as you once led
Continued overleaf

Continued from previous page

Sunday School I thought it might be you."

"Yes – but what about my pickles?"

Josie hoped she did not sound selfish but a great deal of hard work had gone into making those preserves.

Gracie remained firm.

"We can find someone to sell them. Let me tell you more…"

Time sped by. Soon folk would flow in. Josie tried to work faster, aware that when she finished here she had her own booth to prepare.

Two youngsters from Sunday School were playing tag around the hall and generally getting in the way. What they needed was something to do!

"Maisie and Aiden, come over here please."

Once a teacher always a teacher! The two youngsters obeyed.

"Mrs Watts, we miss you telling us off in Sunday School," said Aiden, cheekily.

"Never mind that now. You can both help me fold these tickets, please…"

Soon the job was done and Josie scurried to her new stall. It was festive – but it had little to do with a stable in Bethlehem.

Still, she loved children and as the day sped by her resentment melted and she began to enjoy herself. A sneaky glance told her the pickles were going well. Josie said a silent sorry to God for her uncharitable thoughts.

By four o'clock she was exhausted. Selling pickles was easier than what she had done today.

Not so much fun though, said a little voice in her mind.

"No," she agreed aloud. "That's not so much fun."

Before starting to clear up, everyone gathered in the kitchen for tea and mince pies and the consensus of opinion was that the bazaar had been a huge success, including the face painting and the balloon modelling man.

Gracie beamed.

"How was it, Josie? You looked as if you were having a great time."

Josie admitted that Pots and Pickles would have been lonely without Colin. Their new vicar was one shrewd lady.

She threw back her red hood and removed her snowy beard. Her one condition when she agreed to be Santa was a traditional costume.

"Actually, Gracie –" She took a bite of mine pie then added, "I'm missing Sunday School and… well, I did have a thought about Easter. We could do an Easter egg hunt, and for that you'll need an Easter Bunny…"

• •

THE AUTHOR SAYS…

"I was not happy when I was asked to swap duties at a church event but like Josie, I found it was not so bad after all. Maybe there was a story here…"

FANCY THAT!

Fascinating facts for **geeky girls!**

The first ever space shuttle had less computing power than the average smartphone today

✦ The word "geek" was originally used to describe circus performers doing amazing feats.

✦ The Hulk was originally grey but Marvel changed him to green after issues with the ink in their presses.

✦ The temperature of the Earth's core is as hot as the sun – 5,500 degrees C

✦ The symbols used to censor words in comic books are called jarns, quips or nittles – lumped under the generic term grawlixes.

✦ 80% of people eat their corn-on-the-cob in circles rather than from side to side.

✦ When awake, the human brain produces enough electricity to power a 40-watt light bulb for 24 hours.

✦ It would take 1,200,000 mosquitoes all sucking at once to drain the average human of blood.

✦ A "jiffy" is an actual unit of time: 1/100th of a second.

✦ Under a microscope the structure of ice cream is almost identical to that of lava.

✦ The first house in the world to have its electricity supplied by wind power was in Kincardineshire, Scotland – in 1887.

✦ People who play computer games are less likely to have nightmares than those who don't.

The word "brainiac" comes from the Superman villain of the same name

WORDS: BABS BEATON PICTURES: ISTOCKPHOTO, REX/SHUTTERSTOCK

A Little Rain Must Fall

Love has the power to overcome all obstacles, as our tale of two very different weddings reveals

by Patsy Collins

Maria

The church is booked. Invitations, trimmed with ribbon matching the bridesmaids' dresses, accepted. I'm excited about how many of the items from our wedding list have been promised. The bridal bouquet, six bridesmaid posies, corsages for the mothers, and a dozen buttonholes are ordered. We've tasted the wedding breakfast, evening buffet, champagne for toasts and wine to accompany the meal. I've checked the table decorations match the bridesmaids' dresses and groomsmen's cravats. It's going to be perfect.

All I have to do now is stick to my diet and hope it doesn't rain. I'll just die it if rains; it would ruin everything.

Amari

Please let it rain. Everything will be OK then. The grain will swell, crops grow and we'll be able to eat. Rain produces sweet grass so the goats give rich, nourishing milk. Perhaps we'd even have enough to sell, so I can buy cloth for my wedding dress. Fresh water in the well will allow us to clean our homes, our clothes, ourselves. We'll stay healthy. We will live if it rains. I'll get wed if I live.

If the rains don't come in the next month we'll see withered fruit drop from the trees and stunted crops blown away with the dust. We'll sell our books and furniture, the beginnings of our new home, to pay for food.

I watch a tear fall onto the dry earth. I don't let another follow it.

Please let it rain.

Maria

The forecast says it might rain on my wedding day. I can't help crying.

Dad hugs me. "A little rain's not the end of the world," he says. "The top can be put up on the car we've hired.

"I'll ask the people erecting the marquee to close the side panels and you and Dan can look round for nice places inside that'd make good backdrops for your photos."

"I suppose you're right." I hope he is. It's too late to change the date.

Continued overleaf

Special Day

"What's up, love? Just the weather or something else?"

"The rain's enough, isn't it? What'll Dan's family think if I arrive bedraggled and the reception is a washout? They don't like me much as it is."

"They will when they get to know you, love. Wedding nerves might be hiding your best qualities."

It's not just for Dan's family I want it to go perfectly. Mum and Dad had a quick wedding because his regiment was ordered to Northern Ireland. Mum wore a hastily altered, borrowed dress and the reception was in a pub. They say they didn't mind and it's the years afterwards which matter, but they set up a savings scheme for mine so I know they want a big fancy do this time.

Please don't let it rain.

Amari

I heard Fadil singing before I saw him today. He sings of the rain that's coming. Coming very soon, too, according to his grandfather. I've never heard that man tell a lie.

I join Fadil's singing as we help prepare for the rain. We clear ditches to channel it to our families' wilting crops. Fadil climbs up to check the roofs on the grain store and barn. If we're lucky enough to have food to store, we'll not let it grow mouldy and rank.

We bring in anything which the rain could spoil. How strange to think that the very thing which will make everything right can also damage a book of poetry, a rack of drying figs.

It will come, I'm sure of it. The animals are restless and I can even smell moisture on the air.

Maria

When the cars arrive, the bridesmaids and Mum dash out as the first fat drops fall. The driver of my car holds a huge umbrella – in totally the wrong shade! – over Dad and me.

"Text the photographer and make sure it doesn't appear in any of the pictures," I instruct Dad. It hardly matters. The whole day is already spoiled. Walking up the tree-lined gravel path to the church will make my dress filthy, the open air dance floor will have to go into the marquee making it cramped, and angry tears are threatening to smear my make-up.

"There's a message!" Dad says.

"Ignore it and call the photographer."

"I'd better not – it's from Dan's best man." He reads for a moment, then asks our driver to pull over.

"What's happened?" I demand.

Dad doesn't want to tell me but I insist.

"There was an accident. They're waiting for an ambulance."

Amari

The rains have come! Huge fat drops, sending up clouds of red dust as they land. Soon small streams run everywhere. What music it makes as it gurgles through the ditches we've made and bounces off the tin roof.

Fadil spins me round as we laugh and dance in the rain. We sit when we're dizzy and talk eagerly of the feast we shall have on our wedding day.

I'm sure I see the vegetables swell as Fadil describes fat golden pumpkins and corn. I smell the meats roasting and feel the sharp tang of cheese in my mouth.

Maria

Oh, Dan my love, please be OK. But perhaps it's another member of the wedding party who needs help? They'd wait for any of them. I try to think of something non life-threatening that could need an ambulance. I don't mind the delay, not really, not if everyone is OK.

"Here, take this."

I look up to see the driver offering me a pack of tissues.

"Your make-up will smudge if you're not careful."

"What does that matter?"

"All brides want to look perfect on their wedding day." He angles his mirror for me.

"And are they all as irritable as me?"

"No, you're by far the worst."

Somehow that steadies me. If it isn't Dan who is hurt then most likely it is someone travelling with him and he'll need me to be strong, to comfort him, not need attention myself. I tidy myself up as Dad passes on the news of the delay.

Amari

Our wedding day at last. There's no sign now of rain in the sky, but its effects are visible all around. The smiling faces of our guests are healthy, flowers

He'll need me to be strong, to comfort him – not to be in need of attention myself

The rain washes my face clean of the melon juice that my imagination is trickling down my neck.

There will be enough food for everyone on our wedding day. Our union will be blessed by the joy of our family, friends and neighbours.

bloom everywhere and tables are bending under the weight of food that has been prepared for the feast.

It's the most perfect day… and I'm perfectly happy.

Continued overleaf

Maria

Dan's fine, love. There was an accident but it wasn't his car."

I breathe a huge sigh and hug Dad. Soon I'll be able to hug Dan too.

I learn a cyclist had been knocked off her bike right in front of their car. The driver called for help, the best man and Dan gave first aid. That included covering her with Dan's jacket, which is ruined.

Dan is OK and will be there to marry me. Our friends and family will be there to share in our special day. Those are the things which matter, not the colour scheme or if I arrive with mud on my hem.

Dad says, "Dan can borrow my jacket for the photos. Good thing they're the same even if mine is shorter."

Our wedding starts late, thunder rumbles during the service, we leave church under a rainbow of umbrellas and confetti sticks to everything. The pathway to the pretty bandstand we'd selected as a photography spot is under water so we have Wellington boots, as well as the wrong colour umbrellas, in the photos.

Dad's speech is interrupted by a call as he forgot to switch his phone to silent. It's a message to say the cyclist is coming round after her operation and expected to be fine, so he adds that in. His speech gets way too long with far too many toasts.

The marquee doesn't leak, but condensation drips down on us.

My new husband whispers, "I love you."

I'm perfectly happy.

THE AUTHOR SAYS...

"As a keen gardener I'm often pleased to see the dark clouds most of my friends would rather be without. For some rain isn't just welcome, but vital."

Blueberry Silver Dollars

What better way to start the day than with these gorgeous little breakfast pancakes!

Preparation time: 15 minutes
Cooking time: 15 minutes
Makes: 12
Calories per serving: 67

Ingredients
+ **200g flour**
+ **2tsp baking powder**
+ **2tbsp sugar**
+ **1 egg, lightly beaten**
+ **250ml milk**
+ **120g blueberries**

1 Mix flour, baking powder and sugar in a bowl. Gradually whisk in the egg and then the milk to make a smooth spoonable batter.

2 Mix in the blueberries. Heat a griddle or large frying pan, non-stick or lightly oiled. Measure dessertspoonsful onto the griddle.

3 Cook the small pancakes until they're bubbly and the edges are firm. Turn and cook the other side until golden. Cover and keep warm.

Cook's tip: Serve with maple syrup, fruit compôte, cream or ice-cream.

RECIPE AND FOOD STYLING: JANETTE MARSHALL PHOTOGRAPHY CLIVE BOZZARD-HILL

Match Of The Day

Peter and I were very happy. We just didn't share many of the same interests…

by **Camilla Kelly**

For the third time I raised my book and tried to read a page; for the third time Peter broke my concentration to tell me about West Ham's new striker.

"Look!" he said excitably, pointing at the TV, where West Ham was involved in some sort of playoff or another. "Did you see what he did with the ball there?"

I gave him my best *Not now, I'm reading* look but he was too absorbed in the match to notice.

I tried again, lifting my book. Heathcliff and Cathy were racing across the moors, peeping in through the windows of their fine neighbours. It was my sixth or seventh time reading *Wuthering Heights* and the romanticism still got to me. I gave a sigh of pleasure.

"REFEREE!" Peter bellowed, making me jump out of my seat.

I might as well give up.

Are you still reading, love?" Peter asked as I got into bed beside him, book in hand.

"Still? I didn't get any reading done this evening, what with the running commentary on West Ham's tactics."

He had the grace to look sheepish.

spine. "*I had Cathy by the hand, and was urging her on, when all at once she fell down. "Run, Heathcliff, run!" she whispered. "They have let the bulldog loose…*"

"Keep going," I said, resting my head on his shoulder. "You've got a lovely voice, you know."

Flattered, he straightened his shoulders and carried on reading. It was a very different experience to hear the book aloud rather than read it myself. It made the scenes vivid in my imagination all over again – just as they'd been when I first read the book as a teenager, nearly twenty years ago.

Eventually, close to sleep, I said reluctantly, "You can stop now, love, if you like."

"No way!" He turned the page to the next chapter. "I've got to find out what happens."

It became a habit after that for him to read me a chapter in bed at night. I looked forward to hearing him read as much as I looked forward to the next part of the story.

"This reminds me of when we first got together," I told him a few days later, when we were getting into bed. "When you were away training at the electrical plant and you used to call me up at night and tell me all about everything that had happened in your day, and I used to listen to your manly northern accent and barely take in anything you were saying…"

He laughed. "You soft southerner, you."

"You know," I said casually, rubbing hand cream between my palms until the smell of orange blossom filled the whole bedroom, "you can actually go and visit

Continued overleaf

"Sorry. I got a bit carried away."

"That's OK," I said, smiling despite myself at his boyish expression. "But do you mind if I leave the light on so I can finish this chapter?"

"Course not."

We were creatures of habit. He did his thing, and I did mine. I snuggled down and reached for my glasses.

"Bother! I've left my glasses downstairs."

Was it worth to hassle to go down in the cold to get them? I was so cosy…

"What's so good about this book anyway?" Peter said, taking it from me and bending back its already cracked the place where Emily Bronte apparently set *Wuthering Heights*. And you can go into the parsonage where she lived. It's a museum now."

"Hm," Peter grunted, checking his mobile phone for messages.

"It's only a couple of hours' drive from here, actually."

"Is it now?" he said, still not looking at me, but his voice all-knowing.

"We could do it there and back in a day," I went on cajolingly.

He scratched his chin.

"Awful long way to go for a day."

"But wouldn't it be interesting to see it? To see where she sat and wrote, and to

Peter, who was generally much more of a townie and tended to panic if there wasn't a Tesco Express and a Starbucks within walking distance, didn't complain once. In fact, he seemed to enjoy it almost as much as I did.

He even did a slow-motion run along the moor yelling, "Cathy, come back to me!" which had me in fits of giggles.

It was lovely to see the parsonage and learn about the writer I'd been such a fan of for most of my life; to stand where she stood, and see what she saw. And it was even better to do it with Peter.

At one point, I looked at him while pretending to be interested in the guide who was telling us about where the Bronte

He even did a slow-motion run along the moor yelling, "Cathy, come back to me!"

wander across the moors?" I poked him. "Plus, I hear they have some really good pubs up there."

He put his phone down and laughed.

"Well, I suppose we'd better stay overnight, then."

I was surprised but delighted that Peter seemed keen on the trip. We went for a long weekend, and the first thing we did was take a long walk from Haworth to Top Withens – the ruin that had supposedly inspired Emily Bronte.

It was a chilly but bright day, and the landscape was the most beautiful thing: golden and green, the sky glorious. We passed the Bronte waterfall, and sat on the Bronte chair – the rock where the Bronte sisters used to sit and tell each other stories.

sisters took tea, and felt a rush of affection for him.

I wanted to do something special to let him know how much I appreciated his coming with me. So I booked dinner in a posh restaurant, and spent ages getting ready at the B&B.

I washed and styled my hair, which had been wind-blown and wild all day, put on my favourite dress and spritzed myself with the perfume he'd bought for my birthday. Shiny and happy, and full of anticipation for the evening, I went downstairs in the pub where we were staying to meet him.

"Oh, hi, love," he said, when I found him at the bar. I'd had to tap his arm to get his attention, and he barely glanced at me. "Be right with you…"

Not quite the reaction I'd been hoping

for. The problem was, there was a football game on.

A few other men were sitting around watching the massive TV screen above the bar. They all winced as one when a foul was committed, and all cheered in unison when the referee duly awarded a penalty.

I slipped on to the stool beside Peter.

"So, the restaurant's not far from here," I started to say.

Peter nodded absently.

"The thing is," I said, "the table's booked for twenty min–"

"See this fella here," Peter said, gesturing to a bearded footballer in blue, "he's one of the best penalty takers in the world. We just have to see this."

I sighed. "Ok."

The penalty was taken; a goal was scored. I had to admit, it was pretty impressive. It seemed to please most of the audience in the pub, even those who didn't support the team.

Peter turned to me, grinning. "Did you see that? What a goal, huh?"

"Yeah," I said, smiling. "What a goal."

"You look nice," he said, finally noticing. "What time did you say you've booked the table for?"

"It's OK. We can stay here and watch the match and have a bar supper later. It looks like a good game – it would be a shame for you to miss it."

He looked at me sceptically.

"Really?"

If he could visit the Bronte museum for me, I could watch a football match for him. He'd shown me how much more pleasurable it was to share your passions with someone. If he loved football so much, I could at least try to understand what it was in it that made him so enthusiastic. I might even become a little enthusiastic myself.

Who knew that after fifteen years together, there was still room to get a little closer to a person?

I phoned to cancel the booking then ordered a beer and settled down.

"Tell me again the name of that guy who just scored?" I said.

He pushed his bag of crisps towards me and grinned. It was all worth it for that wonderful smile.

Then he started to tell me all about the best striker in the world – and for once, I did my best to listen.

THE AUTHOR SAYS...

"Some people (who don't read) take the fact that you've picked up a book as a sign you must be bored and desperate for an interruption..."

A Family Day Out

Who could have predicted the drama that was waiting
to surface at the peaceful swan sanctuary?

By Della Galton

A wonderful day out for all the family – see the baby cygnets, sample a cream tea in our delightful log cabin café, stroll around our beautiful gardens.

The poster made it sound idyllic.

I was sold on the idea anyway. I loved family days out, even though our family was pretty scattered these days.

My two boys worked on the oil rigs alongside their father, which meant they all had big chunks of time away from home. Tanya, my eldest, was married with a little one – but at least she lived close by with her husband.

Mum was close by, too – I'd checked the swan sanctuary had wheelchair access. Not that Mum necessarily had to be in a wheelchair, she could walk a little way, but she was less trouble sitting down.

The last time we'd taken her on a family day out (Farmer Palmer's, that time) she'd missed falling in the duck pond by a hair's breadth and then she'd trodden in something unmentionable so we'd had to drive home with the windows down.

And then there was Kate of course.

Kate was my youngest at thirteen. She was a late addition to the family; I'd mistaken her for the menopause.

Teenagers had been tricky enough the first time. Round two was a challenge of gargantuan proportions.

Not that Kate was into wild parties and staying out all hours like her elder siblings had been. On the contrary, Kate was a quiet little thing. She almost didn't seem to belong in our rowdy, untidy family. She'd been scared of her own shadow from the moment she'd toddled far enough to have one, and at thirteen she wasn't much different.

Kate cut herself off from the world with her iPod and a curtain of hair. She took part in the barest minimum of conversations, and then she spoke infrequently.

When I went to see if she fancied coming to the swan sanctuary I found her in the spare room, which Mick uses as an office-cum-man den when he's not away on the rigs. She was searching through a drawer full of old papers.

"What are you looking for, love?"

She jumped guiltily when I spoke.

Continued overleaf

Continued from previous page

"I need some ID to open a savings account," she muttered, her face turning scarlet. "I thought I could use my birth certificate, but I can't find it."

"I'm not sure where it is, either – why don't you take your passport? And don't I have to go with you if you're opening an account?"

She muttered something incoherent and stomped out of the room. I stared after her, puzzled. She wasn't usually snappy. Although I had noticed she'd been ultra-sensitive lately.

I'd put it down to her age; all those hormones swirling about – teetering on the cusp of being a woman. I remembered the turbulence of being thirteen very well.

and she beamed, displaying pink teeth – I'm sure those lollipops couldn't be good for her. But I was pleased Lucy was so outgoing, although as Tanya often said, I didn't have to live with her.

"I haven't had a decent cream tea since 1976," Mum remarked, clutching her chunky knit cardigan around her as we drove out of our estate. "I hope they've got clotted cream."

"Course they'll have clotted cream, and real strawberry jam too," I said, keeping my fingers crossed. I'd checked for most eventualities – I'd checked that the car park wasn't too far away from the venue. I'd checked that the swan sanctuary was on flat ground. I'd even checked that they hired out wheelchairs,

I'd checked for most eventualities, but the quality of the cream tea I'd left to chance

"Do you fancy going to the swan sanctuary on Sunday?" I called hopefully after her retreating back.

She didn't answer, and I was quite surprised when on Sunday morning she came downstairs just after breakfast and announced she was coming with us.

"It'll be great fun," Tanya said enthusiastically, as she fastened baby Lucy into her car seat. "Ducklings are adorable – don't you think, Kate?"

"What about the ugly duckling?" she muttered, and I thought I saw tears in her eyes. I was about to ask her what was wrong when Lucy started yelling.

"Want to see swans." She waved a pink lollipop in the air. "Want to see big swans."

"We will, darling," Tanya promised her

but the quality of the cream teas was something I'd left to chance.

At least the weather was nice. The sun beat down on the backs of our necks as we paid our entrance fees. Mum settled uncomplainingly into her hired wheelchair and tucked an old tartan rug over her knees, just in case.

Lucy wasn't so impressed with having to hold on to her mother's hand.

"Let go. Want to see swans!"

"Yes, but we don't want you falling in the water, do we, love? You can't swim as well as a swan."

Kate did her own thing as usual, strolling ahead of us along the gravel path, peering into the dark estuary. There were swans everywhere, snowy-feathered proud birds gliding gracefully through the water, or sitting unconcerned on giant, twig-strewn nests close to the path.

Even Kate smiled as we saw our first cygnets, with their fluffy grey feathers and dark beaks. Two men came along the pathway behind us, pushing wheelbarrows filled with bird seed, and I realised we'd arrived at feeding time.

As a small crowd gathered to watch, one of the men began to give a running commentary on the swans.

"They don't usually nest so close together," he told us, his voice echoing out of a speaker beside the path. "And they don't have to nest on this part of the estuary – the swans aren't restrained in any way – but we feed them three times a day and they seem to like the full board arrangement."

Several of the audience laughed as he threw out a scoopful of seed and the flock surged towards it.

"The downside is that sometimes we have territorial spats and also it's difficult for the cygnets to bond. Usually they'd only see their own parents in the first few days of their life, but here they tend to see a lot of swans and so it takes them longer to work out who's who. It can take as long as two weeks for them to bond properly."

I stared out across the reedy banks of the estuary – I don't think I'd ever seen so many swans in one place. There were few spats over lunch – they obviously knew

there was plenty of food to go round.

"Also," our guide continued, "because there are so many swans nesting here, we'll have the odd one who won't want to sit on her nest at all. She'll sneak up to another bird's nest and lay an egg there – knowing it'll be taken good care of and she won't have to do any of the work."

I felt rather than heard Kate's reaction. I was still standing next to her, our arms touching, and she quivered. When I turned to look at her I could see there were tears running down her cheek.

"Love, whatever's wrong?"

She shook her head violently and stomped away; a slender dark-haired figure in red T-shirt and jeans, her arms hugged tight around her.

With a quick glance around to make sure the others were all still listening to the commentary, I headed after her along a gravel path and through an archway of trees.

"Kate, love, wait." I caught up with her by a fenced-off section of water which housed a single swan and its shimmering white reflection. I rested a tentative arm around my daughter's slender shoulders.

"What on earth's the matter?"

"Nothing."

She didn't shrug me off, though, which was a good start.

"Well, something obviously is." I stroked a section of her hair away from **Continued overleaf**

Continued from previous page

her face. A strand stuck to her wet cheek and my heart ached for her.

"Kate, love, please talk to me. This isn't like you at all."

"I'm adopted, aren't I?" she finally managed through a series of gulps. "That's what the girls said at school. They said you were too old to have me and I don't even look like you. So I must be."

Shocked, I stared at her. It was the longest speech I'd heard her make for several weeks and it got me to the very core. I held onto her shoulders gently and made her look at me.

"You're not adopted, sweetheart. I promise you. You're a Jenkins through and through – same as the rest of us."

"Your gran's got dark eyes," I pointed out, gently. "And she had brown hair too before it went silver."

"You're saying I take after Gran?" She stared at me incredulously. "She's not exactly quiet though, is she – she's just as loud as you lot."

"Actually I never was loud until I had five children to contend with," said a voice behind us, and I realised Mum had abandoned her wheelchair and followed us along the path. She leaned heavily against the fence, her face a crease of concern and the buttons on her chunky knit cardigan clinking against the wood.

"I was a dreamer just like you, Kate, when I was growing up. I used to get that written on all my school reports. It was

I realised that Mum had abandoned her wheelchair and followed us on the path

For a split second hope flared in her dark eyes. Then she shook her head.

"I can't be." Her voice was flat. "That's why you wouldn't give me my birth certificate, isn't it? I found everyone else's in the drawer, yours and Dad's and even Tanya's, but mine wasn't there."

So that's why she'd been so upset.

"It must be somewhere else, darling, I'll find it for you later. But why ever did you think you were adopted?"

"Anita Parkins said it. We're doing genetics in biology and I don't have the same colour eyes. Or hair. You're all blonde and I'm not. And you're all really noisy. And I'm not." She gave another little soft sob.

I could see where she was coming from, but I was desperate to reassure her.

only when I had my kids that I got loud. I had to shout to be heard above the row at the dinner table."

Kate obviously found that hard to believe, which wasn't surprising – Mum had the loudest voice of any of us. Besides, it's difficult enough to imagine our parents being young, let alone our grandparents.

"And your mum's right about the brown hair, pet. I looked just like you when I was your age. Beautiful," Mum added with a wistful expression. "I'll dig you out some photos when we get back."

Kate glanced between us uncertainly.

"So I'm really not adopted, then? I've been worried about it for ages."

"But why haven't you ever said?" I stroked her cheek tenderly.

"I didn't want it to be true. I kept hoping I'd wake up one morning and look in the mirror and find I had your blonde hair – or at least maybe Tanya's confidence." She fiddled with a splinter of wood on the fence and glanced at the swan a few feet away, almost motionless on the dark water.

"When I was a kid the ugly duckling was my favourite story. One minute he was grey and ugly and the next he was blonde and beautiful."

She blinked a few times and I blinked too. Why hadn't I noticed her pain?

I knew the answer to that. I'd been too busy babysitting for Lucy and trying to cope with running the house single-handedly while Mick was working away.

Not to mention fixing things at Mum's house too. Mum had had drama after drama lately. Her washing machine had flooded the kitchen floor and it had needed retiling. Her boiler had needed replacing. It had been traumatic to say the least. I hadn't noticed my youngest daughter was having a trauma that was going on right under my nose.

I reached for her hand. She let her fingers stay in mine, quite limp, before looking up at me through her tear-washed eyes.

"Then just now when that man said about the swans laying eggs in other bird's nests, well I thought maybe that's why you brought me here – so you could tell me I wasn't yours." And suddenly her fingers

weren't limp any more, but digging into mine, tight with longing..

"Oh darling." I wrapped my arms around her and she put her head against my shoulder. "Of course you're mine and I know you're not as rowdy as the others but really that's not all that surprising. They had each other to argue with. Even though you're not an only child, it must have felt like it sometimes – what with them all being so much older. Of course you're going to be shyer."

At that moment Tanya came round the corner pushing Lucy's buggy. Kate pulled back and stuck her chin in the air and looked at me pleadingly.

"You won't tell anyone why I'm upset, will you?"

"I won't tell anyone anything, darling. I promise."

Much later we sat in the log cabin café. Tanya and Lucy and I ate chips and Mum got her cream tea – with clotted cream and real strawberry jam. Kate said she'd like to try one too, but could she substitute cola for the tea?

"I always thought scones were for old people," she said, sneaking me a glance. "But they're quite nice actually."

"Good," I said. "You'll be drinking tea, too, next news."

"Ugh! No way."

"I got this fact sheet about swans in the **Continued overleaf**

Continued from previous page

shop," Mum said, wiping her fingers on a paper napkin and handing Kate a leaflet. "It's quite interesting. It says that cygnets go white like their parents when they're about a year old, but often they don't get the yellow beak for another year. It's not an overnight thing, but the genetics catch up eventually."

She winked. Kate looked at her intently, before dropping her gaze with a smile.

I swallowed a lump in my throat and thought that my mum and Kate were certainly cut from the same cloth where sensitivity was concerned. Tanya hadn't noticed any undercurrents – she was wiping ketchup off Lucy's face before it spread to her dress.

Perhaps that's what all families do, I thought with a flash of insight – avert a series of small disasters before they turn into great big ones.

I shielded my eyes against the sun and said to no one in particular. "Oh, I do like a nice family day out, don't you?"

Kate nodded emphatically, and beneath the table she reached for my hand and squeezed it tightly.

"Me too, Mum," she whispered.

● ●

THE AUTHOR SAYS...

"The idea came for this story after a chat with a friend whose teenager was going through a tricky patch, and a day out at the swan sanctuary."

Brain BOOSTERS

Kriss Kross

Try to fit all the listed words back into the grid.

4 letters
Guff
Isle
Lino
Peer
Skua

Weld
5 letters
Booby
Coypu
Rural
Seamy

6 letters
Gunman
Menace
Oboist
7 letters
Cohabit

Curious
Tableau
8 letters
Euphoria
Molasses
Optimism

9 letters
Messiness
Stabilise
Uniformed

Birthday Surprise

My best friend and I are about to give her boyfriend a special message he's unlikely ever to forget...

By Lydia Jones

"Y ou OK?" Meg enquired.

"Fantastic. I feel a total idiot."

"I think you look kind of cute."

"Thanks a bundle, Meg. I can hardly breathe in this thing."

I try to take a breath through the mouth hole of the costume's huge rabbit head; bits of plastic fluff stick to my lips.

"Do you want to try walking in it?"

I experiment putting one clumpy paw in front of another.

"It's like walking in a deep sea diving suit," I complain.

"And you'd know because…?"

"Just saying."

"What about a bit of a sexy bunny wiggle?" Meg giggles. "You've got such a sweet fluffy tail."

"You might be my best friend, Meg Simmons, but don't push your luck, OK?"

"Sorry." She looks immediately contrite. "I really appreciate you doing this Terry. You're the best mate ever. I mean that."

"I can't think of anyone else in the world I'd turn myself into a singing telegram for."

Meg tries to give me a hug but can't manage to get arms around me; we both laugh. She checks her watch.

"We'd better get going."

Her face flashes anxiety. I know she wants this to go well.

"Come on. Let's go and give James a birthday he'll never forget."

I smile, then realise that of course she can't see, so pull the cord that operates the flirtatious bunny wink.

Getting in the car is, naturally, a right performance. I can't sit properly because of the fluffy tail and my enormous grey thighs get in the way of Meg's gearstick.

"OK. Let's do it." I turn to clip my seat belt across the bulging fur stomach and whack Meg in the eye with one of my big floppy ears.

"It's fine. I've got another one."

Meg gives a little breathy laugh. I watch her, dabbing her eye, putting on a determined face and I am flooded with affection. We've been friends since forever, so when she asked me to do this as a special surprise for her boyfriend's birthday I could hardly say no.

Personally I've never liked him – far too smooth and full of himself – but I wouldn't say that now. I pull the wink cord again which makes us both laugh and then we set off before I can change my mind.

"You sure we got this right? This is pretty swanky."

We pull up outside a seafront fish restaurant. I spot James's sports car parked across the road.

"He said he was meeting a client here."

Looking expensive in mini-dress and heels, Meg slinks in behind me

"Well, he's certainly in for a surprise. OK. Here goes nothing."

I lumber out of the car seat to be confronted by a snooty-looking doorman in dark blue livery.

I try a flirtatious wiggle and pull the wink cord; he is unimpressed.

"We don't want your sort in here. This is a classy establishment."

Looking expensive in mini-dress and heels, Meg slinks in behind me.

"It's for a birthday," I plead with him.

He scowls and turns.

With much wiggling I retrieve my just-in-case fiver from the costume's pocket and with my back to the door, press it into his hand. Suddenly it seems I am suitable.

Continued overleaf

I stumble through the smoked glass door and hover uncertainly. Pristine tables with arrangements of carnations and candles in cut-glass domes stretch out beneath subdued lighting. Outraged forks clatter onto china plates as some of the closest diners catch sight of me. I am absurdly grateful for the huge bunny head to hide my face; through its mask I see Meg stationed near the back wall.

Stalling, I pull the wink cord at a distinguished looking chap on a table nearby. He almost smiles but is immediately berated by his wife who shoots me a look to freeze hot soup.

I scan the sea of starched white tablecloths. Where is James?

All at once I spot his immaculately styled head in a very close encounter with a svelte looking Cheryl Cole clone. She's laughing softly at something he's said and gazing adoringly.

This is her, then – the "other woman" whom Meg has finally found out about.

At first she was heartbroken and then angry. But now she's calm. I am so proud of how she's handling this; that in spite of everything she still has so much spirit. She is ready to put it behind her and move on but first, for the sake of all that James and she shared, she has organised this birthday surprise. I hope I manage to pull it off.

With the aim but none of the accuracy of an arrow I wobble between tables. My furry legs tug at tablecloths; people grab hold of their wine glasses in panic.

"Sorry. Sorry," I whisper as they tut and pull back in disapproval.

I focus on my target through eye slits. He clinks glasses with Cheryl's clone; he has no idea what's coming.

Finally my furry feet reach a space beside James's table. I give a theatrical bunny wiggle to make sure everyone in the restaurant is watching.

"James Moreton?" I say, as if I'm checking. When I start to sing *Happy Birthday* James looks embarrassed, but also a bit pleased. He always has loved to be the centre of attention. But what I say next wipes the smile from his face.

"Hooray! Happy fortieth birthday, Dad!"

"*Forty?*" The Cheryl clone looks as if she has swallowed something very unsavoury. "You told me you were thirty and what's this about children?"

"Nothing, darling. They must have the wrong person."

James' face is looking as white as the tablecloth.

"And Mum says," I continue, enjoying his discomfort, "she's so sorry you have to be at a business meeting on your birthday but she's baked a lovely big cake and we can all celebrate together tomorrow night."

"*All?*"

Cheryl-clone's eyes are pieces of flint. For once in his smarmy life, James appears to be speechless.

"The twins wanted to come too." I'm improvising; speaking louder now that diners at other tables are listening openly. "But they had to be in bed. They're only ten, you see," I confide to Cheryl-clone in a stage whisper behind my paw.

The glossed red lips form an "o" shape. I watch her watching James as his face turns from white to pink to purple-red.

"You have a wife?" She leaps to her feet. "*Three children*?"

Red-tipped manicured fingers find her handbag, a blingy designer specimen.

"It's all starting to make sense now – all those awkward clients who demanded you meet them at night. You unbelievable *creep*!"

She starts to take swings at James with the bag. He covers his face to fend off blows. People at neighbouring tables nudge each other.

"But Sasha, sweetheart – it's all a mistake," he protests, to no avail.

"Don't you 'sweetheart' me. A mistake? You're dead right there's been a mistake – and it's mine, for ever believing a word you said."

With that, she turns on her extremely high stiletto heels and stalks out.

James is still a most unattractive beetroot colour. His vanity will have been seriously wounded by me adding ten years to his age but he does have a family from a previous relationship, although I may have embroidered details the teeniest tad.

I clap furry forepaws in a job-done gesture. This is such an upmarket place to be publicly humiliated, I'm willing to bet that James won't be bringing any more women here.

"Who are you?" he hisses, dabbing his face with a napkin where the corner of the Cheryl-clone's bag caught him.

"She's my best friend," Meg says, stepping forward.

"Meg, darling – I can explain."

"Way too late for that, James." Her face is sad but determined. "But you should know I've been careful with all your stuff. It's packed in black bags on the street. You'd better get over to my place – you know it's bin day tomorrow."

James's mouth makes an ugly codfish gape.

Meg links my arm. As we walk towards the door, the whole restaurant is applauding, especially the woman who was so snooty at the start.

Even the doorman gives me a high-five – though he doesn't go so far as to return my fiver.

With another victorious bunny wink we exit.

"Oooh, that's a bonus," Meg giggles when we get outside. She points to where Cheryl's clone is carving patterns on the paintwork of James's sports car with a key. "Better than we could have imagined."

I play-punch her shoulder with a huge grey paw, knocking her off-balance.

"Excellent. Now let's get back to my flat so I can ditch the fur and we can celebrate the most memorable birthday James has ever had."

• •

THE AUTHOR SAYS...

"I was recently in a restaurant when a diner was subjected to a singing telegram and I thought how much more mortifying it would be if the surprise wasn't a pleasant one."

Helping Grandpa

The directness of youth can be a real tonic when everyone else is tiptoeing around on eggshells

By Jo Styles

Sitting on a chair on the hot patio, Lisa could hear voices drifting up from behind the gnarled trunks of the old apple and the ash tree at the bottom of the garden.

"Grandpa, stop being so spiky."

Little Clara was always accusing her grandfather, Martin, of behaving like a hedgehog these days.

Lisa could just imagine her dad carefully smoothing the irritation from his brow. "Sorry," she heard him say.

Paper crackled. Plans were being studied yet again. Martin and Clara were making a Wendy house. Well, actually it was more like a palace – or even a castle in the air, the way Martin had drawn it.

"Grandpa? How long will it take?" Clara asked.

"I'm not sure, Petal."

Lisa detected a hint of doubt in his voice. Ever since he'd returned from his holidays and had a bout of the flu, he'd left all his self-assurance behind.

She left her seat and wandered down the meandering lawn. At its end Martin and Clara stood in the shade of the conifer hedge, peering at planks of wood. A jam jar full of nails stood close by, so did an electric drill and a big toolbox.

"Everything all right, you two?"

Martin swiped the damp strands of white hair off his forehead.

"Yes, everything's fine," he snapped as if she'd accused him of something.

Lisa gazed down at his plans, pinned to the grass now by four round stones. The local planning department had assured them no permission was needed for a child's playhouse, even when they were told Clara's castle would be on stilts.

A few days ago all the wood had arrived on a lorry. Lisa and her husband, Tom, had hefted it down to the shady part of the garden.

"Just let your dad get on with it, Leese," he'd said. "It'll take his mind off things."

"We'll make a start in a minute," Martin said now, before one of his under-brow glares shooed Lisa away. Grandpa-and-granddaughter time didn't care for trespassers.

Knowing she wasn't wanted, Lisa returned to the patio. Soon the sound of drilling drifted down to her on the breeze.

The noise carried on for twenty minutes before the din of the drill was drowned out by a scream.

"It's a wasp! Grandpa, it's a wasp!"

Continued overleaf

"Stand still," came Martin's sharp reply. "Don't flap at it, you'll make it angry. Don't run, Clara."

Clara came shooting out from under the shade of the apple tree, her skirt flying, her scream shrill and terrified. On the patio she thudded into Lisa's arms.

"It's a wasp!" she yelped, spinning and batting wildly at the empty air.

"I think you outran it," Lisa said gently. "Grandpa will deal with it."

Clara heaved in a deep breath.

"He's spiky today. I told him." She gave a proud smile. "You're as spiky as a hedgehog, Grandpa."

"And what did he say?"

"Sorry. He always says sorry. Then he's spiky all over again."

"Clara, the wasp's gone now," Martin called from the bottom of the garden.

"Go and help him," Lisa said. "He needs you, Clara." She nudged her daughter back down the lawn. "I'll go inside and fetch some lemonade."

Clara was lying flat in the grass when Lisa returned with refreshments. The little girl flinched every time her grandad thumped at a nail with his hammer.

The hammer slipped suddenly, Martin hit the plank instead with a hollow whack. He growled like a bear, one hand sliding across his chest.

"Are you all right, Dad?" The glasses on Lisa's tray rattled in alarm.

"Will you please stop asking me that?" he snarled.

"Fine." Lisa didn't meet his gaze. She set down her tray then sank down to the grass, careful not to say another word as she handed out their drinks.

Clara frowned as she took her glass.

"Are you grumpy as well today, Mum?" she asked. "I don't know what's up with everyone. You're so spiky all the time."

Martin studied the leaves on the old ash tree. He wouldn't explain. His family and friends were like spies sneaking around, whispering behind his back the things they daren't say to his face.

"Can I have some biscuits, Mum?" Clara scrambled to her feet before Lisa had time to say yes or no. "Do you want some, Grandpa?"

"No, thank you," he said as she pounded towards the house. He peered around at the mountain of wood as if challenging Lisa to ask, *Can you really do this, Dad? Isn't it too much, too soon?*

His cheeks flushed. He wiped his brow.

"I think you were right," Lisa said. "I'm glad we didn't tell Clara. I mean, it would only have frightened her at the time and now... well." She couldn't just smile at him any more; she was never sure how he'd react to even that. "I mean..."

"She can still tell me off," he said bluntly. "That's what you mean, isn't it? She's the only one left who's not terrified I might keel over at any second."

"Dad..."

"Well, it's true."

"Well. Yes. She can still tell you the truth, I suppose."

"And that's how I like it. I want her to tell me straight. No excuses. No pity."

That's as much as he ever said. He shook his head, looking as muddled as the bits of wood scattered across the ground.

He'd been fascinated by the mechanics of the procedure his surgeon had explained at the hospital months earlier.

"It's a bit of plumbing," Mr Cooper had explained cheerfully, as if Martin's heart were simply a sink unit and his arteries nothing but lengths of copper piping.

Lisa suspected her dad had ignored the chapter in the booklet he'd been given entitled *Dealing With Your Emotions after Surgery.* He'd never been interested in those. Then the mood swings had swamped him, dark depressions drifting in like sooty clouds. Now six months later, he still struggled with his feelings, as if Mr Cooper had bypassed all the love of life his heart had once contained.

"It was a big op, Dad."

"I know. I was there."

He replied with a snort.

Lisa sat thinking of all those worried faces that had hung over his hospital bed: relatives and friends but never, ever Clara. To her, he'd gone to Wales for a two-week holiday. He'd fed chips to seagulls on the chilly beach and tugged Grandma into the sea for an icy paddle. Then, when he got back home, he'd caught the flu.

Clara came skipping back, biscuits in hand. She skirted the wood as she munched, leaving a trail of crumbs for the birds. Then she skipped over to Martin and kissed his cheek.

"What's that for, then, love?"

"To make you less grumpy."

"I'm not as grumpy as I was, am I?"

She measured his grumpiness with her hands. "You're still *this* grumpy. Grandpa." She smiled. "Can Mummy help you now?"

It was Lisa's turn to study the old ash tree, its leaves as unsettled as her stomach. She was so used to being angrily shooed away now. They all were.

"It's no good just me doing it," Clara went on. "Who's going to help you when I'm at school, or with my friends, or swimming or having a riding lesson?"

"That's a good point," Lisa dared to add.

Clara confronted her grandpa as nobody else would. She cocked her head and stuck out her lip.

He gave in, his voice low and level.

"All right, Mummy can help me too, and your daddy as well. Even your grandma can pitch in, if she wants to."

It seemed he intended to get this job done even if his well-made plans had to be scrubbed out and redrawn.

Yes, Lisa was glad they kept the truth from Clara.

She met his gaze. His lips turned upwards. It might not yet be a real smile but at least he'd managed to fix one together.

"What do you want me to do next?" Clara asked.

"Oh, you've done enough already, Petal," he said. "You're doing everything Grandpa needs."

"Even when I say you're being spiky?"

He laughed and hugged her.

"Especially when you tell me that," he said. "That's when you're helping Grandpa most of all."

• •

THE AUTHOR SAYS...

"While I was seeing a friend in hospital an elderly gentleman on the ward was visited by his granddaughter. The little girl didn't seem impressed by his irritable mood. 'Grandad, stop being so spiky!' she said."

The Girl Who Sailed The World

Nearing the end of her solo voyage, what fills the exhausted thoughts of young sailor Carly?

by Camilla Kelly

A twenty-minute nap taken in complete exhaustion doesn't give you much chance to dream, but Carly managed to.

She dreamed of her mum and dad. Not as they had been, waving her off from Falmouth four months ago, but from much longer ago: pulling up in the family car while she waited at a campsite, Mum with a raised eyebrow, all concern; Dad rubbing his eyes tiredly. Just after

And has she managed to fix the generator?" asked the journalist.

"She has."

"She's had to know that boat top to bottom. I think she gets her engineering skills from her mother," Adam said.

"He's teasing." Joan bumped against her husband. Goodness knew where their daughter's skills had come from.

After the interview Joan and Adam walked down to the busy harbour. The interest in Carly's single-handed non-stop navigation of the globe had been

"As if you wouldn't have driven twice as far when you heard her sobbing on the phone"

midnight. Both waiting for an explanation of why they'd been called to drive for hours to come and fetch her.

Then Carly jolted awake to the creaking and groaning of her wind-bucked boat and all its demands. The autopilot had gone down and she had to navigate the final distance herself.

She was alone – and still many miles away from home.

encouraged by Carly's sponsors, but there was a great deal of genuine pride – especially among the locals – in the achievements of the young sailor.

Assuming she made it back in one piece, Joan thought, superstitiously touching wood. Carly had been in frequent contact by satellite phone but that didn't stop Joan worrying.

"It should only be an hour now," Adam

said, taking her arm reassuringly.

Oh, but those hours were dragging!

"I think I did something silly," Joan said, stopping suddenly.

"Why, what have you done?"

"I was chatting to that girl, Arabella – you know, from the local paper? And I ended up telling her about Carly and the Brecon Beacons."

"You didn't!" Adam said, appalled and amused at the same time.

Joan covered her mouth, turning bright pink all the way up to her hairline.

"Carly will never forgive me, will she?"

Adam laughed.

"I don't think I've forgiven *her* yet. Making us drive seventy miles to pick her up in the middle of the night."

"But she was feeling so homesick, love. Don't you remember your first trip away from home?"

Adam sighed, playing the put-upon dad.

"As if you wouldn't have driven twice as far when you heard her sobbing on the phone," Joan chided affectionately.

"I would have had a hard time picking her up from the middle of the ocean if she'd got homesick, wouldn't I?"

"That's why I told Arabella the story. I **Continued overleaf**

Continued from previous page

really can't believe it's the same girl."

Joan had tracked Carly's progress faithfully on the map: the seventy-foot-high waves beyond Antarctica; the great stretch of landless ocean between New Zealand and Cape Horn. The blisteringly hot days, the snow and ice days, the star-strewn nights she'd never be able to fully imagine. All this her daughter had seen.

"Do you know what Arabella

Her dream had remained in her mind all that day. Adam was wrong; she'd never forget that ill-fated camping trip to Brecon when she was thirteen. Without that experience, she'd never have been able to undertake this journey.

Her heart tripped faster when she came close enough to make out figures waiting on dry land. Her exhaustion left her, and long before she was brought in and set foot ashore, buzzing with excitement

The blistering heat, the snow and ice, the star-strewn nights, all this she had seen

said then?" she continued after a pause.

"Hmmn?"

"She said maybe Carly felt she had something to prove."

Adam shook his head resolutely.

"I doubt she ever thinks about that trip to Brecon now."

One of Carly's friends had written *Smooth seas never made skilled sailors* in waterproof black marker on Carly's racer. It was one of a blizzard of good-luck wishes, but it was the one to which Carly kept returning to.

She touched it now, as Falmouth Harbour came into sight and the sailboats and cruisers full of tourists, reporters and well-wishers who had flanked her for the last miles sent cheers and applause volleying across this final patch of sea.

and still swaying as if there were waves beneath her feet, she'd picked Joan and Adam out of the crowd.

What she had learned in Brecon was the lesson that no matter how far she went, home was always there. As it was here now, in those two familiar figures. The courage that conviction gave her was beyond measure.

She grinned broadly at the sight of their proud faces. That was the dearest sight in the world.

THE AUTHOR SAYS...

"When I read about young sailors who go out on long single-handed journeys I always wonder where they got their courage – and of course, how their families must feel."

ILLUSTRATIONS: ALAMY

FANCY THAT!

Fascinating facts for **Nature Girls!**

An African Grey parrot called Alex may be the first animal to ask an existential question: he asked what colour he is

The Earth is slowing down by about 17 milliseconds every century, so in about 140 million years we'll have an extra hour each day.

✦ Hummingbirds are the only birds that can fly backwards.

We know more about the surface of the Moon than we do about the bottom of our oceans.

✦ **The octopus has three hearts.**

✦ Lemons contain more sugar than strawberries!

The Bombardier Beetle shoots boiling hydrogen peroxide as a (very effective!) defence mechanism.

✦ **Kiwis lay the largest egg in relation to their body size of any species of bird in the world.**

✦ The apple is Britain's national fruit and botanically is a member of the rose family.

✦ **Butterflies can taste with their feet.**

Flamingos can bend their knees backwards

✦ The Atlantic Ocean is saltier than the Pacific Ocean.

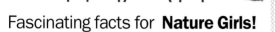

WORDS: BABS BEATON PICTURES: ISTOCKPHOTO. ALAMY, REX/SHUTTERSTOCK

Softest Sea

The delicate blue scarf didn't seem to belong in this lonely, isolated spot – rather like me, in fact...

By Mhairi Grant

"How did that get there?" I asked, picking up the scarf lying on the lawn.

"The wind probably," said Mark.

The blue scarf was made of the softest wool and slid through my fingers. For a moment I imagined Mary Poppins, with umbrella up, descending from the sky and demanding her scarf back.

"It's cashmere," I murmured.

Cashmere or rough-spun cotton, it made no difference to Mark. He was eager to be gone.

"Well, I'd better get those quality control tests done."

Mark worked for the Water Board and a few moments later he headed off to the

A city girl born and bred, I hadn't appreciated the insistent food demands from the local wildlife.

I went to my art studio, a spare room really, and put the scarf down. Only hikers or those who fished came here, and then rarely to the cottage unless to get a fishing permit. Neither set were given to wearing expensive scarves.

"But someone's lost it," I murmured, thinking how I used to wear high-heeled shoes and frequent wine bars.

I looked at the scarf again. It was out of place and it tantalised and teased with possibilities. It was like a muddy welly sitting in the middle of Oxford Street.

I stared at my canvases. They were of landscapes and wildlife, except for one. It

To the call of a wood pigeon and the sound of squabbling ducks, I began to paint

far end of the reservoir. A breeze rustled the trees in the conifer plantation nearby.

Yet it wasn't enough of a wind to snag and sail a scarf through the air.

Swans swam towards me. I was their last resort for food when there were no boats on the reservoir. I made myself scarce. Jemima and her gang would come right up to the cottage if I let them.

had started from a poem which made me laugh. A woman was slowly changing into a donkey and her family didn't even notice.

"Not your usual," Mark had said, when I showed him the picture of the woman complete with donkey ears and tail.

True, but the woman did exist. She had turned up at my door weeks later, minus the ears and tail, looking for a field for her

donkey. Now the scarf, together with the Mary Poppins image, refused to go away. *Come on, Freya, what's keeping you?*

I hurried to gather together my paints. And to the call of a wood pigeon and to the sound of squabbling ducks, I started to paint. Later, as the shadows lengthened and the sound from the reservoir and woods ceased, I switched on the radio.

So," said Mark that evening, "how's your day been?"

"Fine, I argued with a DJ, sang along with The Arctic Monkeys and produced a new painting. Do you want to see it?"

Mark loved my paintings but my latest piece was met with a muted *Hmm*. I should have taken the hint. But I was **Continued overleaf**

Continued from previous page
never one to keep my mouth shut.

"Don't you like it?"

"It's well executed, Freya. But – well, a fairy?"

"She's not a fairy. She's a woman wearing a soft blue cashmere scarf who happens to have wings."

"It's as weird as your donkey woman. Freya, you should get out more – and learn to drive."

I sighed. It wasn't as if I hadn't tried that. Four failures were all I had to show for my attempts – and a marriage almost ended before it had begun.

"I know, but the driving school won't have me back after I crashed their car."

Mark held me close. "The isolation's getting to you, Freya. You know it is."

husband who was stressed beyond endurance was no laughing matter. But neither was my family and friends being three hundred miles away.

We'll see," I murmured into his chest. Then I went to put my *Woman With Wings* painting in a prominent position. I was optimistic. It had worked once before – even if I never saw the woman again.

Still, after a few days I decided I needed help. I tied the scarf to the gate post. There, it fluttered in the wind and acted like a lighthouse beacon.

Sometimes I found myself longing for the smell of petrol fumes rather than manure

"It is not!" I protested.

Country life just took a bit of getting used to – that was all. But country life was in my blood and I really loved it. My great granny used to live in the Scottish Highlands and stayed where it took a day trip to get to the nearest shop. Family folklore said that she'd been a bit of a Spey Wife and could predict the future.

I was supposed to take after her.

"Freya," he said, exasperated, "you have a name for each swan and duck on the reservoir!"

"So?" I challenged. "If I had a car I would give it a name as well."

"I should try teaching you again."

But I didn't want that. Living with a

Sometimes as I looked at it, I would send out thoughts to the universe. *Send me a friend, send me a friend.*

But I wasn't my great-granny. I brought the scarf in when it started to rain.

Instead I phoned my mother and friends incessantly.

"Everything's fine," I would tell them, sometimes longing for the smell of petrol fumes. It would make a change from the smell of manure and the coconut scent wafting from the gorse.

Sweaty bodies came later when I joined an evening Zumba class. I was the youngest there, and had to decline coffee afterwards because Mark picked me up.

Still, it was a start.

Next it was the local book group. It was during the day. I had to walk a mile and a half to the bus stop and then kill time waiting for the bus back.

Still, I enjoyed the discussions. Gavin, one of the other members, and I had a taste for psychological thrillers. We were in a minority of two.

"We're not budding axe-wielding murderers with a screw loose!" we'd argue, laughing.

It was fun, and I regretted I couldn't go to some of their other gatherings.

"You'd be most welcome," I was often assured warmly. But it would mean someone going miles out of their way to take me back home. I didn't feel I knew anyone well enough to allow them to do that, even though a few had offered.

Yet I was considering the possibility on my way to the next book group when a car stopped.

"Do you want a lift?"

The accent was American and the woman young. The combination stopped me in my tracks and I stared at her as if she had wings.

"Yes please. I'm going to the bus stop."

"I'm going into town if you want," she offered when I got in. "I believe they have a book club there."

"You don't like psychological thrillers, do you?" I hardly dared hope.

"Love them, they're my staple reading."

"Yes!" Gavin and I could do with some back-up. "That's where I'm going!"

"That's great! I would have gone sooner but I had to fly back to the States and only got back a few days ago."

Flew – she flew. I pinched myself then to make sure I wasn't dreaming. I took a deep breath.

"You haven't lost a soft sea-blue cashmere scarf, have you?"

"I have – a couple of weeks ago. My husband and I have bought Ferniebank. Why, have you found it?"

Ferniebank was just over the hill! I nodded and grinned. The woman grinned back. Then our words tumbled out and leapt over each other as we exchanged our life stories. It was like coming home to a warm fire on a winter's day.

Her name's Becky. She's a nature writer and interested in my paintings, and is talking about a collaboration," I said to Mark later that day. "And we're going for a night out in the town soon."

Mark was shaking his head.

"What is it?"

"It must be in the genes after all. Do you know what you should do now? Get into that studio and paint a picture of a driving instructor with nerves of steel and the patience of a saint."

Now, that was a thought! Already the picture was forming in my head. But the instructor wouldn't be driving a car – she would be wearing plated armour and driving a tank…

THE AUTHOR SAYS…

"I walk regularly round this reservoir which is beautiful but isolated, and I have often wondered what it would be like to live there."

Something Beautiful

Green shoots of new life and hope can appear in the most unpromising of circumstances…

By Gillian Harvey

S o, how's the pain this afternoon?" Kelly looked keenly at Phil and could already see from his ashen face that his leg was worse than it had been earlier.

"Oh you know, not too bad." He grimaced, shifting slightly in his seat. "You don't have to do this, you know."

They both knew this was a lie. Ever since he'd come off his bike three weeks ago, he'd been unable to cope on his own. It was only the fact that his sister, Grace, said she'd help out that enabled him to leave the rehab unit they'd put him in.

Then Grace's son had developed chicken pox – and, as Kelly was the only neighbour who seemed to be around during the daytime, Grace had come knocking on her door.

"It's no trouble, honestly." Kelly smiled – although in truth it was difficult to fit in the three necessary visits per day. She'd just taken on two more accountancy clients and was rushed off her feet.

That said, she had to admit she'd begun to look forward to the enforced break from her computer and obligatory cup of tea that her visits to Phil necessitated. It was nice to chat with a real human being, rather than someone on the other end of an email. She hadn't realised, until this week, how lonely she'd started to feel.

It was early autumn, and the days were short and gloomy. The leaves on the cherry tree in the front garden she overlooked from her office window were blushing orange and breaking from their stems to form a carpet at its feet.

She'd thought that setting up alone would be beneficial to her – she would no longer have to see Stuart every day at the office, and running her own business would increase her confidence and motivate her to reach higher.

Instead, she was like the tree, she realised, when the bright fruit and tender leaves were stripped bare and it was left, exposed, vulnerable and robbed of its beauty and interest.

She'd expected to feel a bit lonely at first, when she'd quit her job in London to go solo. Harry, her boss, had warned she'd be "back within the year," that she'd miss the company, the guaranteed salary.

And she did. Yet she didn't miss the
Continued overleaf

hour-long commute, horrendously expensive season ticket and the stress of meeting deadlines imposed by someone else; nor seeing Stuart, with his casual enquiries about how she was doing.

Plus she still had friends locally; her salsa class on Thursdays; and Friday evenings in the pub with the girls. Perhaps it wasn't loneliness at all – she just had a touch of the autumn blues.

"So, how's work?" Phil asked, interrupting her thoughts.

"Oh, you know. Dull as always."

"Come on, there must be something interesting going on."

"You do know I'm an accountant?" she joked. "Nothing interesting ever goes on!"

He smiled at her. "I bet you get to see all sorts of dodgy financial deals. If you want real boredom, you should try being a mechanic like me. It used to be OK, but these days it's more about plugging in a computer and doing what it tells you.

"Probably not much different from your work. It's only the racing that keeps me sane." He looked ruefully down at his leg. "and it's not like I'm going to get to do that for a while." He chuckled, but there was pain in his expression.

She thought of her own bike, sitting forlorn and cobweb-covered in the garage at her parents' house. She'd used to enjoy riding out with Stuart, in the days before the arguments; the divorce.

Now she didn't care whether she ever rode a bike again.

She looked at Phil's left leg, tanned and muscular, contrasting wildly with the thick chalky cast on his broken one. You could tell he was a cyclist, just by the size of his calves. They'd barely spoken in the past, but she'd see him every morning going off to work. Eight-thirty on the dot every day, past her office window – a flash of colour as he built up speed.

Then one day he hadn't been there, and she'd heard about the accident. The drunk driver. The injuries that would have killed him, had it not been for his cycle helmet.

Now, ten days into her role as temporary carer, she knew more about him than she knew about some of her closest friends.

There was something about the situation – her caring for him; him sitting there helpless – that led to a kind of intimacy. She'd found herself talking to him, too, about her work, her friends... her divorce.

When she'd poured her heart out to him, she'd been a little embarrassed afterwards as if she'd given too much away. Yet he'd seemed to understand, talking to her about his own relationships; the son he rarely saw.

She doled out his painkillers as instructed, and watched as he took them; each one so large that it made him grimace as he swallowed. The colour returned to his face shortly afterwards, although his speech began to slur slightly.

It was why he didn't like taking them, she knew – they made him a bit spaced out for a while. However it wasn't for much longer, she kept reminding him – hoping it was true.

As she stepped outside and walked the short distance to her house, she noticed the tree again – the myriad colours of the leaves at its base – copper, amber, sunshine-yellow and rich chocolate brown. They were so vibrant, so bright, that they seemed to soften the starkness of the tree's bare bark. It looked quite pretty, she realised.

Later when she popped around to give Phil his evening meal, he was asleep; the TV playing some awful programme in which two men bought old cars and gave them a makeover.

His head lay slightly to one side and his cheeks were flushed. His breath was calm, his stomach inflating and deflating like a baby's.

The phone rang and she picked it up without thinking.

"Oh, hi Kelly, it's Grace," said the voice on the other end. "How are things going?"

"Not too bad – I think he's struggling a bit with the pain, but otherwise he's in good spirits."

"Thanks so much for helping us out."

"It's no problem, I've quite enjoyed the company." It was a platitude, but suddenly Kelly realised it was true. She'd enjoyed talking to Phil, even when he'd been speaking about his cycling – something that always reminded her of Stuart.

It was the way he talked – the humour in his voice, the stories he recounted. And something more – something she couldn't quite put her finger on.

Grace laughed.

"Well, luckily Will's completely better, so I can take over again from tomorrow."

"That's great!" She knew she should feel relieved – knew she should be pleased that Grace's son had recovered from the chicken pox and that she would now be able to catch up on her work – but somehow she couldn't bring

herself to smile. Placing the receiver back in its cradle, she looked again at Phil and felt a frisson of regret.

She would miss him.

She woke him up gently when she'd finished preparing his pasta.

"Oh, and I heard from Grace," she said casually as she left. "Will's better, so she'll be back tomorrow."

"What a relief!" he said, with a smile – seemingly so happy that she didn't say what she'd planned to: that she'd like to see him again; that she'd enjoyed his company.

Sitting at her desk the next day, she saw Grace whizz past in her blue two-seater, and drive off again just five minutes later. Phil had admitted to her that he and his sister weren't very close, and she thought again of her long conversations with him – had they been as important to him as they had to her?

Yawning, she turned her attention back to the row of figures on her flickering laptop screen. She was behind – it wasn't like her. She usually had the ability to throw herself into work and be completely absorbed until it was done – but today her attention kept wandering to the house two doors to her left and the man sitting there alone, resting his leg and worrying.

Eventually, she picked up the phone.

"Phil?" she said when he answered.

"Hi," he said, sounding slightly groggy.

"It's Kelly." She felt nervous suddenly. "I just wanted to see if you're OK? If you need anything?"

Continued overleaf

Continued from previous page

"I'm fine, thanks." His tone was friendly, but abrupt. "You?"

"Yes, fine…" She searched for words, but none came. "Well, bye, then."

"OK, bye." The line was dead.

She felt suddenly annoyed as she stared at the silent phone on her desk. Ten days of caring for him and he'd barely had time to ask how she was.

Outside, cold rain saturated the grass, and dampened the branches of the tree, which was developing patches of moss on its trunk. She hoped it wasn't dying.

I don't understand why you're so upset," Rebecca said later as they shared a bottle of white. "He's sitting there, in pain, probably just feeling sorry for himself."

"I know, but…" She searched for the words to explain to her best friend how she was feeling. Angry, yes – but more rejected than anything else. She flushed suddenly, realising what she'd wanted him to say; how she'd hoped he'd feel when he heard her voice on the phone.

"You like this guy, don't you?" Rebecca smiled, her hair shining as she reached forward to fill Kelly's glass from the half-empty bottle. "Go on, admit it."

"I don't know." Kelly's cheeks must be as red as a pillar box. "It's not easy for some of us, you know, Rebecca."

Rebecca, with her perfect husband and perfect family. Kelly loved her best friend, and wanted her to be happy, but it was hard having to watch Rebecca's relationship thrive when her own life seemed to have fallen apart.

"Ouch," Rebecca grimaced. "Come on, Kelly, he'd be lucky to have you. Don't let one bad piece of fruit spoil the rest, and all that stuff."

"You're right," said Kelly, reaching forward and giving her friend's had a squeeze. "Sorry, Becs."

Later, when she lay in her too-soft bed in her silent home, she thought back to how she'd felt talking about Phil.

Could she really have been hoping for something to happen between them when she'd only really known him for ten days? Was it just because she was lonely, working from home, or was it because there was real feeling there?

Not that it mattered, she realised, turning over and pulling her duvet around her shoulders. He wasn't interested anyway.

The next day Grace knocked at the door with a card filled in with her looping handwriting, containing a high street shopping voucher.

"Thank you." Kelly had smiled, feeling even more keenly that Phil hadn't enjoyed her company at all – he hadn't even signed the card. "Would you like a coffee before you go? It's so cold today!"

"No, I'd better get back. I like to get home before it gets dark."

"I just hate it when the nights draw in," she'd said. "And everything looks half-dead. I spend half of my day looking at that tree," she gestured to the cherry tree, standing naked and dark in her front garden. "So depressing."

"I know what you mean about the dark evenings," Grace had replied with sudden animation. "But I love autumn! It's the leaves – you know, that crunch under your feet. And the reason the trees shed them. The way they draw the nutrients from the leaves back into themselves – take what they need to nourish themselves through winter. I always think they could teach us a thing or two."

Kelly had looked at the dark tree differently then: it wasn't weakness that caused its leaves to drop, but a kind of strength.

Over the following weeks she got used to seeing the flash of Grace's car passing her window; she'd seen Phil, too, a couple of times, walking gingerly with a stick, his leg now wrapped in a blue cast. He hadn't looked up as he passed her house.

Then Grace's visits had stopped.

Kelly's fingers itched to call Phil again, but something had stopped her – pride, perhaps, or fear.

She turned her attention again to the disappointing profits of the local newsagent, resolving as she did so to put more of her own money into keeping the little enterprise alive. Otherwise she'd have to go to the large supermarket in town every time she wanted a chocolate bar or a box of teabags.

When the doorbell rang, she barely flinched. She was used to getting deliveries around this time, and was expecting her new printer to arrive.

She stood up, feeling her legs ache from sitting for too long.

As she approached the front door, she couldn't see the outline of a person in the bevelled glass and wondered for a moment whether she'd imagined the bell. But she couldn't have. She reached forward and opened the door, feeling the fresh air rush over her face.

There was no one there.

She stood for a moment and the cherry tree caught her eye. As the winter sun shone on its branches, she could see the first shoots had begun to form in readiness for the spring. It wasn't dead or barren at all, she realised, but just waiting for the right moment to come back to life.

And then her smile widened. Leaning against the tree was a bike, with a pink bow stuck to its frame. She knew straight away who it was from.

As they wheeled their bikes back into her front garden after the short ride, Phil leaned against her tree, rubbing his leg and grimacing.

"Is everything alright?" she asked him.

"Yeah, just got to keep building up my muscles," he replied with a wry grin. "I feel half dead, like this tree."

She grabbed his arm and laughed.

"Just wait until summer," she told him. "That tree has the juiciest cherries I've ever tasted!"

She smiled as she thought back two weeks ago and how he'd explained his long silence. How he hadn't wanted her to date him out of pity; he'd wanted to be back on his bike both metaphorically and physically before he asked her out.

She hadn't known whether to be angry or amused at his admission – those weeks of feeling rejected were fresh in her mind.

But then she'd thought about the tree, how each year it renewed itself; moved forward and blossomed again. She'd opened her arms and gathered him to her.

Just like the tree, she realised, she'd needed to shed the old and open herself up to something new; something beautiful.

THE AUTHOR SAYS...

"This story explores the idea that even in the bleakest situation, there is hope to be found. Only sometimes, we need to look a little more closely in order to find it."

L-Plates

Sometimes cold feet need to be taken seriously – at other times, they just need to be gently warmed

By Helen M Walters

At what point should you call off a wedding? Before you've bought the dress? Before you've booked the venue and invited two hundred people to the reception? I'm guessing "at the hen night" isn't a popular choice.

My friends are all here you see, and we're dressed up to the nines; with me in L-plates and them in angel wings. We're meant to be having fun. So why do I feel like I'm watching someone else's hen party from a distance?

Trish tops up my glass. She is saying something, but the music is so loud I can't hear her. So I just smile brightly and hope that'll do.

She shouts a bit louder.

"Is everything OK, Susie?"

I should have known I wouldn't be able to fool my best friend.

"Come on," she says and grabs me by the hand, dragging me out of the bar and along to the ladies' cloakroom.

"Right," she says. "Spill. You have to tell me what's wrong."

"I'm not sure I'm ready for all this," I say, with a sob.

"What do you mean?" Trish asks. "Matt's lovely. Surely you're not having doubts about him?"

"No. It's just that I haven't known him all that long, have I?" I sniff.

"Well, no. But you love him, don't you? Sometimes you just know when something's right."

"I suppose so," I say. "But there's so much I don't know about him. When we had to fill in the paperwork for the wedding, I realised I didn't even know his middle name."

"Oh, you'll learn all that stuff in time," she says airily. "And it's not that important, really. It's how you feel about each other that matters."

"And I have no idea how to be a wife," I wail, the enormity of the situation flooding over me. "My parents didn't exactly make a good job of it, did they? Splitting up before I was five. What do I know about marriage?"

"Hey," Trish says, embracing me in a huge hug. "That's what the L-plates are for. And just because your mum and dad didn't have a good marriage, it doesn't mean you can't."

A lot of crying later, I feel a tad better.

"It's a huge decision," Trish says. "But don't let your fears get in the way of the best thing that's ever happened to you."

"I'll try not to," I say.

"Right. I'm going back out there," Trish says. "The others'll be worried, so I'm going to tell them you're having a wardrobe malfunction and you'll be back out in a minute. Yes?"

"Yes. Don't worry. I'll be fine."

I feel my phone vibrating. It's Matt.

"Hi, love," I say, trying to make my voice as positive as I can.

"What's wrong?" he asks.

"How do you know anything's wrong?"

"Because I know you and I can hear it in your voice," he says.

Tears spring to my eyes again, and I suddenly realise it doesn't matter how long we've known each other, it's the depth of the connection that matters.

"I'm feeling a bit jittery," I say. It feels good to tell him. "I've just realised what a big step we're taking and how much I have to learn. About you, about us…"

"I'm not surprised," he says. "It's a big night for you. That's why I was ringing. To tell you how much I love you, and how much I can't wait to be your husband so we can spend the rest of our lives getting to know each other better."

His voice soothes me and by the time the call ends, I know for sure I'm doing the right thing.

I don't know everything about Matt. I don't know his favourite colour, or whether he prefers his eggs scrambled or fried. But I know the important stuff. I know how to cheer him up when he's grumpy, and that he likes his feet rubbed when he's tired after a hard day at work.

And, most importantly, I know he loves me, and understands exactly how I feel.

So I'm not going to call off the wedding, but I am finally going to enjoy my hen night. I'm a bride, albeit one with L-plates, and I'm going to get married. And suddenly I can't wait. ■

Saving Grace

What could go wrong in the three weeks we were
minding our neighbours' pets? Well…

By Alison Carter

ILLUSTRATION: JOHN BARRIE

The Bennetts, at number sixty-eight fascinated us. The teenage daughter was in a band and had blue hair; the son rode a unicycle; the dad made lager; the mum grew chillies. They owned two dogs, a cat, a rabbit, a snake, two fish and a tortoise.

"We're off for three weeks in Barbados," Maggie Bennett said, standing on my doorstep one day. "It's cheeky to ask, and I wouldn't if our friend who normally minds the place wasn't away…"

"You'd like me to feed your cat?" I said, keen to be neighbourly. "No trouble."

"Thanks," she said. "Yes, the cat. It's just… er, could I come in?"

She sat at my kitchen table, smiling.

"The dogs'll go into kennels. But if you'd be willing to feed –"

"The rabbit?" I interrupted. "Lucy would love to! She's always longed for pets."

"Brilliant!" Maggie exclaimed. Then she paused, one sparkly-nailed finger slowly circling the rim of her mug of tea.

"Your fish?" I said. "Fish are easy, right?"

"Two minutes' effort!" she agreed. "The shake of a canister."

"And the… tortoise eats… lettuce?"

"Exactly!" she said. "Or weeds. Anything!" She cleared her throat. "How might those animal-loving children of yours feel about Dave?"

"Dave?"

"Our ball python. He's a sweetheart."

Since that summer, I have often thanked God that those dogs went into kennels. You see, we're not animal experts.

First, the rabbit died. We think it got a fatal shock when Lucy moved its run. She said later that she wanted it to enjoy some scenery, but the scenery included – we think – a fox. The vet said that it's a speedy way to go.

The cat didn't like us, and began hissing at my husband as soon as the Bennetts left. After a week it was living entirely at number fifty-one, a house in which – my son George reckoned – lived a witch. Certainly when Harry, my husband, knocked and enquired about the cat, the scary lady said it was quite happy, thank you, before slamming the door in his face.

Grace, the tortoise, vanished on Day Two. George thought he saw her trundling slowly past our shed. We asked George why he hadn't turned Grace around and pointed her back towards the house.

"She looked like she wanted to go that way," he said, unhelpfully.

I felt sure we could manage the goldfish, but soon the fat one was getting thinner and the thin one oddly bloated. We asked the vet who suggested they had "displacement anxiety", but do fish really worry when they move next door? Anyway, the poor fish died, within a day of each other which was a blessing.

Dave the snake seemed irritable. I know it seems unlikely that we could read a snake's expression, but I fretted over him so often that I felt I knew his moods.

Maggie's instructions described the need to cuddle Dave, but none of us could manage that, and after a fortnight he left. Unwilling to alert the neighbourhood for obvious reasons, we searched for days, to no avail. The internet advised that Dave was probably happy in the wild and enjoying a diet of mice.

"Let's be thankful the Bennetts didn't leave us a mouse," Harry said.

The day the Bennetts were due back, we sat in a forlorn row in our garden, remembering the dead and the missing.

"I have never felt so mortified," I said.

"If only we had one left," Harry said, "I'd feel better."

"What's that?" cried Lucy, pointing.

Harry looked up. "A snake? Dave!" he called out hopefully.

"Oh, I think it's a leaf," said George. He was close to tears.

"No!" I said. "Look! It's Grace!"

As we watched, a tortoise ambled, one tiny foot in front of the other, across the lawn. It took ten minutes for her to reach our feet, but when she did I sensed the heat of the joy around me. She lifted her tiny shrivelled head. To this day I believe that her expression was full of pity. Then she continued doggedly to the back door.

"What a marvel of nature," Harry said, "is the tortoise."

"They live a tremendously long time," I said enthusiastically. "Did you know?"

"I love Grace so much," Lucy said.

I stood up.

"I'll pop her into her box, shall I?" I said. "Just in case?"

THE AUTHOR SAYS...

"I am sorry to say that this story is utterly true. I hope my mum doesn't read this and find herself recalling that terrible summer!"

A Rose By Any Other Name

Freya had a great deal to learn about her quiet, uncommunicative neighbour…

By Julie Goodall

Freya leaned over the kitchen sink and rubbed the condensation from the window. Bubbles frothed in the washing-up bowl as she began half-heartedly scrubbing at dishes, her thoughts concentrated more on the goings-on in next door's garden than on the job supposedly occupying her.

The thick rubber gloves protected her from the scorching heat and she wiped beads of sweat from her forehead with her sweatshirt cuff. She knew people laughed at her old-fashioned ways, wearing Marigolds to wash up, but she'd seen her mother wearing them over the years and, in her own profession as cake decorator, Freya spent an ordinate amount of time with her hands in bubbly hot water.

She was proud of how smooth and young-looking they still were and wished the same could be said of her facial complexion. In truth, that was unlikely ever to have been the case after the way life had treated her and her son.

As she watched, Daniel crouched down in the dirt beside the chain link fence which barely separated the two properties. She could see the new blue trowel in his hand. John must have bought it. It went well with the little gardening gloves and fork which he had given her son last week and she guessed it was part of a set.

Glad that there was no longer a wooden fence between the houses blocking her view, Freya fiddled with the plates in the bowl, pretending that she was doing something of use.

Outside, John dropped a thin blue cushion onto the ground and Daniel knelt on it, beginning to dig, with John pointing out where he needed to place his small trowel. Little conversation appeared to pass between them but, now and again, she saw the pair laugh.

When he was with the eight-year-old, John's wide-ranging expressions reminded Freya of the endless varieties of flowers and shrubs he grew in his garden. Some were rare and quite unexpected but, when you saw them, they felt so familiar that you couldn't quite believe that you had never seen them before.

Once more the window began to steam up from the heat of the washing-up water so Freya leaned forward, further this time, and eased the window open. A welcome rush of air whooshed through, cooling the **Continued overleaf**

Continued from previous page

perspiration on her forehead, and the glass gradually started to clear. Over the fence, John leant down and ruffled Daniel's hair and the boy looked up at him, a look of adoration on his red-cheeked face.

Freya knew that look – she'd seen it a million times before, when Matt had taken Daniel swimming and shown off his twelve-foot board diving; when he had come home with the miracle of a ticket to Manchester United; when he had returned from work with a lively Dalmatian puppy. With both parents working full time back then, the puppy had had to go back.

But that had been Matt – totally unpredictable and living only for today. Daniel of course, had loved it – the exciting knowledge that no one day would be the same as another. It had been fine, of course, in its own way, but children need some routine and stability.

One day, Matt's unpredictability had got the better of him while riding his 1000cc motorbike. Freya and Daniel's stability had been blown out of the water and their routine, from then on, had become absolute.

A fork slipped through Freya's fingers and clattered onto a plate in the bowl as the phone shrilled beside her. She recognised the number on the display instantly and, quickly, pulled off her gloves, grabbing the receiver before the answerphone could kick in.

"Mum! How are you? Everything OK?"

"'Course it is, love. Looking forward to the warmer weather but all right otherwise. How about you?"

"I second that." Freya shivered as she looked out at Daniel, wearing just shorts and a now slightly small green T-shirt that Matt had bought him. "Can't say the same for Dan, though. He's out in next door's garden. Been there for two hours. He never seems to even feel the cold."

"That's nice. Those two seem to get on so well. The forecast says rain later. I wondered if Dan might like to see that new Disney film. The one with the rescue dogs."

"He'd love to, Mum! He's been nagging for me to take him in the February half term. Shall I drop him over?"

"Don't worry. I'll pick him up at about three."

Freya peered into the top of the slow cooker, calculating how much bolognese there would be.

"Eat with us after, then," she said. "It's spag bol. That OK?"

"Certainly is. Be over at three."

"He'll be ready. Drive safely."

Freya would never have imagined things would turn out this way for her mum and herself, living five hundred yards apart and now both without a husband. Freya's dad had upped and done a runner with his golfing partner's wife after twenty-six years. Apparently, the death of his son-in-law had reminded him that "life was too short to pretend to be happy". Freya had barely seen him since.

Behind her, the timer bleeped and Freya opened the oven, drew out three tiers of a chocolate cake and tested them with a skewer before placing them back in and turning the temperature down a few degrees. She reset the timer for five

76 www.myweekly.co.uk

Daniel was screaming with delight and finally fell into the grass, laughing

minutes, returned to the sink, then pulled on her gloves again.

Glancing out of the window, she laughed aloud, watching John chase Daniel around the garden with a garden rake. Her boy was screaming with delight and, finally, fell onto the grass laughing until John grabbed him and threw him into the air. He caught him with ease and Freya swallowed hard, remembering how Matt used to do that exact same thing.

Daniel was smaller then, of course, and his giggles were even shriller. Freya could listen to her son laughing like that all day.

And how wonderful it was to see John so happy and animated. It didn't seem so very long ago that she had been scared to death to even go round to his house – but the day of the 'tree felling' had altered all that...

In truth, it had been quite a poor excuse for a tree. It never really grew any leaves to speak of and Freya, knowing next to nothing about anything in the garden, had been worried that it might have some disease or another.

The tree not being terribly big, she felt sure that she wouldn't need any permission to lop it down and so, in a fit of temper about her general predicament, took it upon herself to take control. The trouble was, she'd never been much good at physics or maths or anything else of that ilk, and hadn't really taken into account which side she was hacking at.

By the time it began to fall and she knew it was heading in the wrong direction, it was all too late to do anything but stand back and cover her head with **Continued overleaf** her arms. The crunch of the fence seemed to echo throughout the neighbourhood and she felt sure that they must have heard it down at the local shop.

The first thing she did was to grab her mobile phone.

"Mum. Mum! You've got to get round here. No… just come round. I'll explain when you get here. No, Dan's fine but I need you to go round next door!"

It had all sounded ridiculous when she'd actually tried to explain.

"It's just that he always ignores me. He's weird, Mum. I'm telling you. I have tried to be friendly… I always say hello but he never, ever answers. He just nods, if I'm lucky, and turns away. He's either stuck-up or – I don't know – weird."

She just couldn't think of any other word for it. The bloke lived alone, didn't speak and spent his time pottering about in his garden. She had no idea what he did for a living but it appeared to involve a great deal of mud, if the bootscraper outside his front door was anything to go by. Sometimes he disappeared for days at

They picked up Daniel from school, cooked tea and waited. Freya tried not to look at the catastrophe in the garden but Daniel thought it was "ace". Of course, never one to miss out on the action, he insisted on coming round with them.

"Keep quiet and let Mum do the talking," Muriel insisted.

Everyone knew how Daniel's enthusiasm overtook him and his ability to control his tongue.

It was a long time before anyone came to the door and the trio almost gave up. Finally, the door opened somewhat hesitantly and a figure towered above them, standing, as they were, on the bottom step.

It was less than five seconds before the jigsaw fell into place.

"C… c… c…" The man paused and appeared to take a deep breath. "Can I h… h… h…"

"Mum's chopped down a tree in the garden and it's gone and smashed up your fence!"

"Daniel!" Freya blushed at her son's

She hardly dared look at her neighbour but his eyes were surprisingly sparkly

a time and the curtains stayed closed.

Freya waited inside the house until her mother arrived but, despite ten minutes of begging, Muriel refused to do her daughter's dirty work.

"Don't be a lightweight, my girl," she admonished. "I'll come with you, but you're not backing out altogether. He can't be that bad."

Yet Freya knew that he was.

frankness, but felt more embarrassment still at her own relief. To her shame, she'd had no idea whether to help the man out or wait for him to get the words out in his own time. What was the etiquette? It was something she felt she really should know.

She hardly dared look at her neighbour but, when she did, was grateful for his reassuring smile. He nodded, his eyes surprisingly sparkly for someone whose garden had just been demolished. Stepping back, he gestured them inside and then through the house.

It was funny, Freya thought, to be in a house that was a mirror image of her own, although decorated entirely differently. She was a bit of a collector, tending to buy ridiculous ornaments whenever she went somewhere new.

Her neighbour, it seemed, had no such leanings, although Freya did notice they had an identical seascape oil in the hall. So excited was she to see this, she nudged her mum hard in the ribs.

"Ow! What?" Muriel hissed.

"Look." Freya pointed and Muriel nodded her recognition.

"That was from Cornwall, wasn't it?" Muriel whispered. Neither of them mentioned that the holiday had been for Freya and Matt's

tenth anniversary. So much for that.

The guys had gone ahead and the women hurried on, Freya realising that a conversation of sorts was flowing between Daniel and their neighbour. Her son's easy manner made her proud, but less so of herself.

Reaching the back garden, Freya gasped. From this side of the fence, it all looked so much worse. The tree had been taller and heavier than she had ever imagined when she'd first started chopping and now she saw how close it had come to the man's greenhouse.

"Oh my gosh! I'm so sorry! I'll pay for everything, of course," she said rashly,

wondering how on earth that might happen. She had barely enough to make ends meet since Matt had died. True to form, he'd cashed in his life insurance without telling her so he could afford a motorbike holiday in the States.

"Don't worry, Mum. I've already told John I'll help him put everything back together and he said OK. He said he would teach me. I told you you're rubbish at gardening."

Freya's cheeks resembled a blood-red rose but that dazzling smile returned, leaving her in no doubt about John's amusement. Despite his speech difficulty, he certainly seemed to say a lot with his eyes.

"That's really very kind, but…"

"My pleasure." It was John's turn to interrupt smoothly, giving Daniel a wink.

"We'll have to lift it back into our garden," Freya said thinking aloud, but John gestured to his lounge.

"I… I… I've a w…woodburner. I'll keep it if you like. Sh… shove it my way."

"Well… that would be perfect," Freya concurred, relieved.

"Mum thought you were stuck up 'cos you didn't speak to her," Daniel informed their neighbour, loudly.

"Daniel! For goodness' sake!" Freya turned quickly to John. "I'm so sorry," she said, hoping her sincerity came across.

She failed to add any more, sensing that any more smiles of that calibre heading her way would leave her with speech difficulties of her own.

Continued overleaf

Lovely Long Read

Continued from previous page

Mummy, come and see, at John's house! He's culpitated a new flower and says he wants you to see it."

Daniel was practically jumping up and down with excitement and Freya failed to conceal her smile at his mispronunciation. So deep in thought was she that she hadn't noticed her son flying through the kitchen leaving a thick trail of mud.

Freya glanced down at all the dishes she'd yet to wash.

"What – now?"

"Yes, now!" Daniel almost yelled.

"OK, OK," Freya laughed. Her gloves discarded, she slipped on her wellies that stood by the back door.

"In the greenhouse!" Daniel called, racing ahead. "John's been growing it. I don't know how he's made a new flower, but he has!"

"Put the kettle on, Dan. M… M… M… Mum might need warming up."

Daniel dashed into John's kitchen and Freya watched as he filled up the kettle.

"I wish he was that helpful at home," she said, laughing aloud.

"He's great company," John told her. "Reminds me of my b… b… b…" He stopped for a moment, looking thoughtful and slightly sad. "Brother at that age. Meningitis."

Instinctively, Freya reached out and squeezed John's soil-covered fingers. No words could suffice, but now she understood their relationship a little more.

Slowly, John turned away, towards his greenhouse.

"Here," he said, glancing back at her.

"Daniel said you cultivated a new flower. Well, that's what he tried to say!" Freya smiled.

John nodded, but seemed a little reserved, which was unusual now that they all knew each other so well.

He lifted a pot and Freya inspected the most perfect flower she had ever seen. The petals were a delicate graduated pink, and silky to her gentle touch. The aroma was sweet but subtle.

"What is it exactly?" she asked, hoping she didn't sound stupidly ignorant. It looked similar to a rose but she wasn't sure that it was one.

John said nothing. He pulled a small white labelling stick from behind the flower. On it were no words in fancy Latin. Just *Freya*, surrounded by a heart.

Freya looked up in surprise. The blue eyes were close to hers, and quite took her breath away.

"Freya?" she mumbled, but her voice was lost beneath his.

"It's taken some time but… Happy Valentine's D… D… D…"

Freya knew it was rude and against all the right things to do, but she didn't need to hear any more. Standing on tiptoes, she placed her hand on the back of John's neck and swiftly pulled him towards her.

What followed then made words seem completely inadequate. A communication of worldwide web proportions flowed between them with perfect understanding, and Freya prayed that Daniel would decide to take a little longer and not just make a cuppa. Much as she loved him, she hoped he would take forever to brew up a massive great pot.

● ●

THE AUTHOR SAYS…

"I was just sitting, thinking how first impressions of someone can often be so wrong. Our snap judgements can be way off the mark and I thought of this story."

Smoked Salmon Stars

This pretty canapé is ideal for serving with drinks.

Preparation time: 15 minutes
Cooking time: 12-15 minutes

Ingredients (Makes 6)
- ✦ **110g self-raising flour**
- ✦ **Pinch of salt**
- ✦ **1 large egg**
- ✦ **4 tbsp low fat natural yogurt**
- ✦ **100ml milk**
- ✦ **Few drops of vegetable oil**
- ✦ **200g medium-fat soft cheese**
- ✦ **100g smoked salmon, cut into strips**
- ✦ **Dill sprigs and lemon slices, to garnish**

1 Put the flour, salt, egg, yogurt and milk into a mixing bowl and whisk together to make a smooth, thick batter.

2 Heat the vegetable oil in a non-stick frying pan and add tablespoons of the batter to make 12 drop scones, cooking them in batches until the batter is used up.

3 Cool the drop scones, then use a star-shaped cutter to stamp out star shapes from them.

4 Top each star with a dollop of soft cheese (or pipe it if you prefer), then arrange smoked salmon on top. Garnish with dill sprigs and serve with lemon slices.

Cook's tip: Use fresh sour cream instead of soft cheese if you like.

RECIPE AND FOOD STYLING: SUE ASHWORTH PHOTOGRAPHY: JONATHAN SHORT

Last Day Of Term

Can the start of the holidays be the beginning of a new chapter for Simon and the girl he left behind?

By Tess Niland Kimber

Simon fidgeted, checking the time again. It was baking in the car, even with the windows open.

"This summer'll be a corker," his wife Monica had said that morning, giving Willow, their spaniel, some water.

"I doubt I'll notice the weather this weekend," he said. "I'll be too edgy."

"I know," she said, tilting her head to consider his choice of shorts and T-shirt.

"Too surfer-boy?" he'd worried.

"At fifty?" She'd laughed. "More beach bum meets *Steptoe*."

When he'd looked horrified, she'd hugged him close.

"Emma won't mind if you're in shorts or a suit. Although she tries to hide it, she wants to see you. And you definitely want to see her. That's all that matters."

"You're right."

"Always." She smiled. "Now get going. Stop a few times. Drink plenty."

"Yes, Mum," he'd joked.

"We'll be here to welcome her." Her blue eyes held his. "It'll be fine, Si."

Right at that moment he couldn't have loved her more if he'd tried.

Now as Simon waited in the heat for Emma to finish school, he remembered his own childhood – the bubbling excitement and countdown to the summer holidays.

"Can't wait 'til the bell goes," he'd say longingly to his mate Keith,

"Yeah – no getting up, homework or boring revision."

In those last hours, Simon planned fishing trips, circus visits and lazy lie-ins. Before work cast its nine-to-five shadow he'd loved being home all summer.

Today – middle-aged, bearded, grey-haired – waiting for Shipley High to spill out its students at the end of term, he felt that delicious anticipation again.

Did Emma feel the same? Was she joking with her own friends about vegging out, or whatever they called it now?

The sun toasted his arms. July was seeing record temperatures, boding well for a barbecue summer.

Suddenly he wondered if Emma liked barbecues. A searing sadness, tainted by guilt, filled him. He didn't know…

Yes, guilt had tracked him like a CCTV camera, stubbornly tugging him to this day. He swallowed. Could he cope? Or

should he take the coward's route and drive off? Disappear, as he'd been forced to these past few years…

"Stick it out, Si," Monica would counsel.

And so he must. It wouldn't be easy but it would be worth it.

He'd dreamed of this moment for ages. The decision to contact her had been a New Year's resolution. A promise made with enthusiasm as Big Ben chimed in 2017 but, in the cold light of January, had daunted him.

He turned the ignition. Air conditioning huffed like a dying patient. There was no doubt – he was nervous. Unease troubled his brown eyes, reflected in the rear-view mirror. But no matter how terrified he was, he must keep this vow.

Suddenly the bell sounded. He flinched. The gates sprawled open and wearing identical maroon uniforms, pupils bled into the car park like a glass of spilled Ribena.

So many children. Some laughing,

Continued overleaf

some alone, others deep in conversation.

Was that Emma? he wondered. The blonde girl? Or the one with the stripey bag?

Dismissing the couldn't-possibly-be's, his eyes flicked as he sought his daughter.

Would he know her? Would instinct prod, "That's Emma" when he saw her?

He tried to remember how she'd looked when they'd last met at the bowling alley. Wow, hadn't that been awkward? It was the first time he'd seen Emma and his ex-wife Dee in four years.

"Simon," she'd said.

He didn't know how to greet her. With a kiss? He couldn't shake her hand. In the end, he'd settled for a smile but was too nervous; it failed to reach his eyes.

"You used to be good at bowling," Dee admitted, her fair hair dyed red and a net of fine lines he didn't remember surrounding her blue eyes.

"I used to like it," he agreed, waiting for a verbal trapdoor to open, as they moved to the lanes.

Emma made a show of choosing her bowling ball. Anything, he felt, so she didn't have to look at him; the father who'd abandoned her at nine.

If only he could explain that he'd just flipped. That leaving them both hadn't been planned. He'd been a bank manager then but the pressure of work and endless, unreachable targets had driven him to despair.

Dee had tried to help but he couldn't tell her how much he was drinking; how little he slept. Thank God, he'd left on the cusp of his breakdown. He wouldn't have wanted either of them to witness that.

Eventually he'd been admitted to the Hay Unit. His stay had been long and progress slow but his mind and body had healed with their care.

Unfortunately, for Dee, there'd been no going back. He'd understood. She'd felt his abandonment, coming on the heels of so many drunken rows and broken promises, was the final curtain on a failing marriage.

The bank had been good to him.

"Take as much time as you need, Simon," said Jackson, who'd taken over his post when he'd been admitted.

When he'd returned, he was offered a customer services post. He'd loved it. Instead of being swamped by pressure, he'd thrived on sorting out problems. And best of all – he'd met Monica.

"You have a little girl? Why don't you see her?" she'd asked, a few dates in, when they were in that delicious stage of getting to know each other.

"I'm… frightened of letting her down. With mental illness, it can return."

Slowly, Monica made him understand that not seeing Emma was more damaging than being around her when he was ill.

"I want to be a good father – the best. I don't know if I'm up to it."

"I'm sure Emma doesn't want a perfect father – just a dad. You."

At first, he wasn't convinced but Monica's words seeded his mind. He longed to see Emma again.

Initially, Dee refused.

"You can't walk in and out of a child's life like you're in a revolving door."

But Monica made him persevere. Told him to explain his illness to Dee. His ex-wife had been surprisingly understanding and suggested meeting at Shipley's bowling alley.

"Strike!" he'd shouted that afternoon when Dee flattened the pins with one, well-judged bowl.

It broke the ice. Focusing on the game – conversation, eye contact, smiling – all became smoother.

Yet later, he'd fretted, "I wish it was more relaxed between us, Monica."

"Give it time. You've years to catch up. It can't be easy for Dee, either. I've been thinking… invite Emma up here. Let her see you at home. I'll keep out the way."

It was another good idea. He'd run it past Dee who'd said, "Yes – but not yet. Get to know her again, first."

He was impatient but understood that she was right.

So they became Facebook friends – weird, she was his daughter – but it actually worked.

Look at my new photos, she'd text.

And he'd obediently click "Like" on images of Emma poking out her tongue or grouped with friends in the shopping mall.

Yes, over tentative months, they'd built a relationship. Not quite father and daughter but something close.

Now as the liberated students swirled around the car like cherry blossom, he attempted to mentally match those Facebook images to these girls. But there were too many faces to check.

Just as he was ready to give up hope,

he caught her eye and felt a burst of joy. "Emma!"

How stupid to think he wouldn't know her. Hair thick with curls, her chocolate eyes studied him with an expression he recognised; it was like looking in the mirror.

Smiling shyly, she slung her bag into the boot.

"We'll have a great time. There's a cold drink – well, it's probably bubbling in this heat – in the door pocket. And there's crisps if you're hungry." He could hear he was trying too hard. "Sorry, Em. I'm a bit nervous. Well, a lot nervous. I want you to have a good time with us."

She sipped her drink.

"You left me."

It was so sudden. Unexpected.

He rushed to say something, anything, but the explanation lodged in his throat. Dee had advised him to tell Emma when he felt she was ready. He took a breath.

"Yes, I did and I'm truly sorry. I didn't think I had a choice but I see now, there's always a choice. I was ill. It's not an excuse." He reached for her hand. "But I used it as one. Coming back was daunting. But I promise – I'll never leave you again."

"You won't. I won't let you … Dad."

As a faint smile crept across her lips, he felt the years he'd missed slipping away.

• •

THE AUTHOR SAYS...

"My friend has a daughter whose father has not seen her since she was nine years old. I read an article recently about absentee fathers and was surprised by the main reason for staying away. It gave me the idea for this latest story."

ILLUSTRATIONS: REX/SHUTTERSTOCK, ISTOCKPHOTO

A Two Horse Race

There's nothing more formidable than a new granny…
especially when pitted against another new granny!

By Jo Styles

Y ou want us to watch some horses running about?" In Janet's lounge, Diane sat perched on the very edge of a chair, as if the covers had fleas.

"It's a hurdling race, actually," Janet replied curtly. "There are fences." She glanced to the door. Her phone stood in the hall. They were waiting for a call from the hospital. Meanwhile, being together would be torture. As usual.

"And you want us to see if we can pick a winner?" Diane went on. "Isn't that just a little bit… silly?"

"Well, we have to decide somehow which one of us holds our grandson first, don't we? We're always being accused of bickering. I thought this would be a good way to solve the problem – and fill in the time," Janet said acidly, "since your Lucinda doesn't want us anywhere near her while she's in labour."

"I thought that was your Karl's idea, actually." Diane waved a dismissive hand. "I'm simply not the competitive sort, Janet. You know that."

Janet gave a snort at that obvious lie. "….And now in the paddock…" the TV said loudly as she flicked it on. On the screen, horses were being led around a parade ring; a large, hushed crowd was inspecting each one.

Janet often watched the racing in the afternoon. She'd become quite an expert but she didn't want Diane to know that. No – Diane really wasn't the competitive sort at all with her fake posh accent, her expensive clothes and immaculate make-up.

"So which one do you want?" Janet asked her casually.

"Oh, I don't know. Does it matter? It's all down to luck, isn't it?"

It wasn't if you'd been studying form. Janet had done just that after her son's call that morning.

He and Lucinda had decided it might be a good idea if, after the birth, their mothers arrived at the hospital together. Then, their dads could come in later after work. Could Diane, who didn't drive, walk round to Janet's to wait it out?

Janet had frowned. Were their offspring trying to force them to be friends now?

In the lounge, she pointed to a

Bobby Dazzler, a grey, had been sidelined with an injury for months. Other than that, he was the best in the field.

All mounted up, the jockeys started leaving the parade ring.

"They'll canter down to the start next," Janet explained. She leaned forward in her seat. "They're off!" she said moments later. "Come on, Bobby Dazzler!"

"Come on, Prince Charming!"

They both held their breath as their horses sailed over the first hurdle.

"Come on, Bobby Dazzler!"

"Come on, Prince Charming!"

Janet laughed as Diane's cut-glass accent slipped.

"You sound more like a local now."

"I beg your pardon?" Diane's accent returned full force.

"You know what I mean."

"I do not."

The crowd on the TV cried "Oooh!" Horses fell; jockeys rolled across the turf. The camera swept ahead to the front-

Diane waved dismissively. "I'm simply not the competitive sort, Janet. You know that"

hundred-to-one outsider on the screen.

"How about choosing that one, Diane?"

"No," Diane replied with a scowl. A big chestnut then appeared, his jockey just springing into his saddle. "That one. He's nice. What's he called?" A name flashed up on screen. "Oh… Prince Charming."

Janet crossed her hands in her lap.

"The first of our chosen horses to pass the post will count as our winner. If that's all right with you?"

"Yes, that seems fair," Diane agreed.

"I'm having that one." Janet pointed.

runners. A grey flash led.

Out in the hall the phone suddenly started to ring.

"That's it!" Janet cried. "That's the call!" She dashed out and snatched up the receiver, listening all the time to the TV.

"It's Bobby Dazzler. Bobby Dazzler all the way, strolling home!"

She grinned.

"Hello Karl. Oh, how wonderful!" She yelled to Diane, "Our grandson weighs eight pounds precisely!"

Continued overleaf

I won, thought Janet ten minutes later as she drove along in her battered old car.

Diane peered at her from the passenger seat.

"I wonder why Lucinda and Karl were so insistent we arrived together."

"I have no idea." Janet frowned then smiled as she remembered Bobby Dazzler looking so proud of himself in the winner's enclosure.

When they arrived at the hospital, Diane tried to charge ahead towards the

"He definitely has Karl's lips."

"Thank the Lord, he has Lucinda's ears."

"I'd better pick him up, then." Janet flashed a triumphant smile at Diane. "I won, after all."

"Sorry? You what?" Karl interrupted. "Actually, Mum… and Mum. Lucinda and I thought, as a special favour, you could pick him up together – at the same time."

"Yes, Mum," Lucinda went on. "Oh, it's all right; we've worked out exactly how you can do it."

"You did what?" Diane and Janet said

Their children exchanged the weariest of looks as they cannoned off each other

maternity suite. Janet nipped in front as they rounded a corner. Then a wheelchair helpfully slewed across Diane's path.

Janet, bolting ahead, dashed into a lift. It was such a shame that a nurse stopped the doors from closing when she saw Diane pelting towards it, too.

They cannoned off each other trying to squeeze through the door of Lucinda's private room at the same time, both of them red-faced and gasping for air.

"Hello, Mum," Karl said, looking tousled-haired and drained as he sat at Lucinda's bedside.

"Hello, Mum," Lucinda echoed, pale and exhausted.

Their children exchanged the weariest of looks; only Janet and Diane missed it, too busy trying to be the first to gaze into the crib at the side of the bed.

There, their brand new grandson lay swaddled in a blue blanket.

"Oh!" Janet gasped. "He has Karl's eyes."

"He has Lucinda's nose."

in unison. They peered at their children. Then they stared venomously into each other's wide, shocked eyes.

"Come on," Karl said firmly, picking up his mobile. "I want to take photos for our baby album. This is going to be great!"

No, it most definitely was not great.

Half an hour later, in the café downstairs, Diane sat tilting her phone towards Janet so that she could see the photos Karl had sent from his own phone upstairs.

"This is so embarrassing," she said.

Janet peeped through her fingers.

"I can't look at them any longer."

In the photos, both of them were hunched over the crib, hands arranged carefully under their grandson so together they could both lift him inches above his blankets.

The baby had a wide-eyed, stunned look on his face, his mouth a big wide O in every shot as if he couldn't quite fathom out what was happening.

"Why did Karl take so many pictures?" Janet asked. "Surely he could see that we looked like utter fools in all of them."

"Why was Lucinda egging him on?" Diane asked in disgust. "'Just one more, Karl'," she mimicked, her cut-glass accent disappearing again.

"And the name they've picked out? Joshua? It has nothing to do with either of our families.

"They're so bossy lately, aren't they? 'Don't come to the hospital until we call! Come together!'" Her hand whipped at the air. "'Do this! Do that! Stand there! Smile!'"

"Yes," Janet agreed. "I don't know what's the matter with them. In fact, they've been unbearable since they announced the pregnancy." She stared at Joshua wistfully. "He's such a beautiful boy, though, isn't he?"

"Oh, yes," Diane agreed enthusiastically. "He's just perfect. It's such a shame our own children treat us so dreadfully."

"It's as if we're getting in the way," Janet said in disgust.

She frowned then, thinking of the racing commentator on her TV.

They've fallen. Two horses are down.

Crash, they'd gone, horses and jockeys sprawling as they'd collided with the brushwood fence.

"It's as if we're nothing but…

hurdles… to them."

"Sorry?" Diane said in irritation, leaning forward to catch her words.

"Oh…" she added numbly as they registered. "I see what you mean."

A weighty silence fell, as heavily as any horse.

"We need some more hot sweet tea," Diane said at last, waving a hankie under her nose. "I think we've both just had a bit of a shock."

"I'll help you," Janet offered.

Diane blinked.

"You will?"

"Yes, I will. I really don't think that fetching tea should be a competitive sport – do you?"

"I don't think we need any more photo-finishes, that's for certain."

Diane shoved her traitorous phone into the depths of her designer bag.

"No. So let's call it a draw," Janet suggested.

She sent a cautious smile Diane's way, one Diane returned in equal measure.

Off they went back to the counter, two abreast, refusing to compete for once. Both of them were quite determined that their racing days were over.

THE AUTHOR SAYS…

"It's such a competitive world these days. I think that's why I like to remind myself now and again that being a winner isn't always about coming first."

A Diamond In The Dust

A damaged princess tiara, a second-hand cleaner and a ginger cat add up to an unlikely fairytale ending...

By Jennifer Jordan

Millie's favourite sparkly tiara, now sporting a gap where one "diamond" had just fallen out, was clutched in both hands as she hopped impatiently up and down.

"Can you see it yet, Mummy?" she asked, anxiously.

"No I can't, sweetheart," sighed Beth, crawling out rather inelegantly from under the table. "But let's try the Hoover."

Millie watched intently as the carpet was vacuumed. Beth's dad had recently rescued the cleaner from the tip and managed to get it working for her after her old one had finally given up the ghost for good.

It was only now as she emptied the dust-bag onto newspaper that she realised she'd also unwittingly inherited someone else's pile of vacuuming debris. Someone with a ginger cat and a new cream carpet, at a guess, she mused, as she reluctantly started probing.

"Look, Mummy – there it is!" squeaked Millie, plunging her little fingers unheeding into the pile of dust.

Beth looked on in astonishment as her daughter extracted a somewhat grubby but very beautiful diamond ring.

The next day at the school gates Beth smiled as Millie skipped towards her with her new friend.

"Guess what, Mummy? Scarlett and I will be five on the same birthday and we're going to share our party!"

"That's wonderful!" enthused Scarlett's mummy as she joined them, "Let's invite the whole class!"

Beth's heart plummeted. Money was always tight as a single mum; she worked part-time and also ran a small internet business selling knitting yarn, but she was constantly hard up. She tried not to look at Millie's expectant little face as she took her hand to walk home.

"We'll see, darling," she said brightly, trying not to think about her unpaid bills and the dodgy boiler that needed sorting.

Eight weeks later, however, the joint birthday party was in full swing and Millie and Scarlett were bouncing around on a blow-up castle along with the whole of Class 1 A.J.

Beth's mind was buzzing as she stacked dirty plates, but by the end of the afternoon she'd decided that as several weeks had now passed by, she would sell the unclaimed ring.

Continued overleaf

Continued from previous page

Later that evening, feeling shattered after the party, she almost ignored a rather late phone call.

"Hello, I'm Archie Hamilton," said the caller. "My mother lost her engagement ring while she was staying at my house."

"Right…" Beth stifled a yawn. She was in no mood for another time waster.

"I noticed your advert when I laid fresh newspaper under the cat's bowl." continued Archie.

"Ah!" exclaimed Beth, suddenly interested, "and what colour is the cat?"

"Um… ginger."

"And have you had a new cream carpet laid recently?"

twinkle too!" smiled Archie.

"No, she didn't," Millie swiftly corrected him. "That was me."

Beth had the newly washed and twinkling ring all ready. Handing it over to Archie, she immediately noticed his leaf-green eyes and reflected that they were also rather twinkly…

She hastily composed herself as her daughter chatted away. When Archie suggested taking them both to a theme park the following weekend, Millie instantly accepted.

Several months later, after Archie had redesigned her website, Beth's business was flourishing; the faulty boiler was repaired and she'd repaid her dad's

She noticed his leaf-green eyes and noticed that they were also rather twinkly

"Yes," Archie hesitated, "but –"

"Has anything broken down lately?"

"My Hoover packed up," explained Archie wearily, "and went to the tip."

"And the lost ring…?"

"Is a claw setting," Archie muttered testily. "With a cluster of diamonds and a sapphire in the centre."

"Congratulations!" declared Beth. "You've passed the test."

Millie heard the doorbell first and raced to the door ahead of Beth.

"Wow, young lady!" remarked Archie, "What a fabulous tiara!"

"I lost my twinkle –" Millie pointed to the "diamond" that was now dull with glue "– and Mummy found it!"

"I think clever Mummy found my

loan for Millie's birthday party.

One Friday night when the three of them were having their usual treat of supper at the local pizzeria, Millie announced that she and Scarlett would be having a princess party when they were six. She asked Archie if he remembered her finding his mother's ring in the dust.

"I most certainly do." Archie met Beth's soppy grin with a heart stopping smile. "Because I found a diamond too."

• •

THE AUTHOR SAYS…

"After depositing our old, broken vacuum cleaner at the tip I drove away wondering if I should have removed the dust-bag. Something valuable may have been lurking inside…"

FANCY THAT!

Fascinating facts for **Fashionistas**

Ralph Lauren – real name Ralph Lifshitz – started out as a tie designer

◆ Coal tar was used as eyeliner, eyebrow pencil and mascara during the Elizabethan era. It smelled bad, was flammable, and caused blindness!

◆ **The first patent for nail polish was in 1919, and was a pale pink. A girl who wore anything darker than pink was deemed immoral!**

◆ Barbie's first outfit was a black and white striped one-piece swimsuit.

◆ The Manhattan jewellery house Tiffany & Co was founded in 1837 and was the first company to create a mail-order catalogue in 1845.

◆ **Pearls melt in vinegar!**

◆ The rarest type of diamond is green in colour.

◆ In 2005 the original ruby slippers worn by Judy Garland in *The Wizard of Oz*, with an estimated value of $1million, were stolen from a Minnesota museum.

◆ **Lipstick first appeared around 5,000 years ago in ancient Mesopotamia when women ground precious gems into dust to decorate their lips.**

It takes one alligator to make a pair of shoes – 3 to make a pair of boots

◆ **The space suits worn by Neil Armstrong and Buzz Aldrin were created by Playtex.**

Roses Round The Door

…are a complete no-no for dynamic, stylish early retiree Maggie. But what is she so afraid of?

By Linda March

I'm warning you," said Maggie, "there had better not be roses round the door."

"But you love roses, Mum," Shona pointed out, puzzled.

"In their place," Maggie agreed.

"Where better than a cottage garden?"

"Wrapped in Cellophane in the hands of a very handsome man?"

"Mum!" With an exasperated sigh, Shona stopped the car beside a row of three red-brick cottages. While not round the door, roses were much in evidence. Maggie gave them a cursory glance.

"Very nice, but not really me."

"It's the middle one. Let's at least have

Continued overleaf

a look around, now we're here."

"As I said, nice if you like that kind of thing," was Maggie's verdict as they made their way back to the car after viewing the cottage.

"It's immaculate," Shona said, "and in very good decorative order."

"Steady on. You're doing the estate agent's job for him."

"Surprisingly spacious, too."

"Don't forget the well-appointed kitchen and newly fitted bathroom," Maggie reminded her. "Yes, it's all very nice, Shona, but –"

"You're looking for a little place that's compact and convenient, that doesn't need a lot doing to it. How can a smart little house like that not be you?"

"It's not a house, it's a cottage."

"Does that make a difference?"

"I'm not the cottage type."

"Most people would give their eye teeth to live in a cottage in a village like this."

"I'm not the village type."

"No – you're the characterless box in an anonymous block of flats type."

"Living in the city is convenient."

"But now that you're retiring…"

"Taking early retirement," Maggie said with emphasis. "Very early."

"You don't need to live in the city any more," Shona continued. "And it's not as if the village is in the sticks, it's just outside town. You'd have the convenience of shops and restaurants and all the other things you like about city life, but the pleasure of living in a picturesque village."

"Picturesque doesn't cut ice with me. I like city life."

"Villages are friendly. You get to know your neighbours, get involved in… oh, I don't know." Shona searched for inspiration. "Amateur dramatics, the WI."

Maggie gave her daughter a look that could wither a field of roses.

"I'm not the –"

"Friendly type, yes I know." With a heavy sigh, Shona started the engine.

As Maggie let herself into her flat, she felt only vaguely dismayed at Shona's "characterless box" comment. She supposed the place was a little bare, but she viewed it simply as four walls, a place to hang her hat.

Working long hours with a lively team who usually spilled out of the office and into the nearest wine bar, what did she need with picturesque homes or roses round the door? She couldn't remember the last time she'd passed a neighbour in the hallway. Everyone had such busy lives.

Flopping down on the sofa, Maggie looked about her. A stranger would find it hard to believe that she'd lived there for over a decade. She'd put so little mark on the place. Framed studio photos of Shona's graduation and her brother Alistair with his wife and two children gave the only clues that the flat's occupant had an identity.

It hadn't always been like this, of course. Once there had been a family home with pictures and favourite ornaments and, if not quite roses round the door, then a pretty garden where children had played and friends had gathered to drink wine and eat barbecue-blackened sausages.

But that had been a long time ago, before they all left home. First Alistair, then Shona… then Gordon.

It had been hard when Alistair and Shona had left for university, but Maggie had at least been expecting that. It was inevitable, the natural way of things, and she had been so proud of them.

What she hadn't been expecting, the week after Shona left, was Gordon's announcement that he was leaving her to set up home with the young, dynamic head of marketing at the firm where he worked. Maggie vaguely remembered her as the glamorous young woman in black satin at the last company Christmas party.

Gordon wanted no hard feelings, just a swift sale of the house and a split down the middle of their joint possessions. Maggie, dazed and disbelieving, let him take whatever he wanted.

Finally realising on moving day that waking up from this bad dream was not on the agenda, she put her boxed-up share of the family's memories into storage and moved into the flat.

Determined that Alistair and Shona would have their own lives, that she would never be a burden on them or "poor old Mum", she retrained in a career with prospects and now, ten years on, was skilled in computer graphics. The memories were still in storage.

Yet now the lease on the flat was up for renewal and the company she worked for – a victim of its own success – had been bought out by a larger concern.

The redundancy package had been too good to turn down, and, with her contacts and experience, she planned to work freelance from home.

Home. Yes, that was the problem, Maggie thought as she swung her legs off the sofa and headed for the kitchen. She had to find a new home that was suitable to work from.

As she finished filling the kettle, the phone rang.

"Hi, Mum."

"Alistair, how are you?"

"Fine. Just to let you know I'll be over on Saturday to see that cottage."

"Ali, I've already told Shona – I'm not the cottage type."

"Whatever. I'm just interested in you making a sound investment."

"Are you speaking in your professional capacity, or as the son who stands to inherit half of all I own?"

"Mother, how could you? But put it this way, if we can get you well set up in a sound investment, watch out for the banana skin at the top of the stairs! See you Saturday."

Maggie grinned. With his wicked sense of humour, Alistair could always make her smile. But this must mean that he and Shona had been discussing her – that they were worrying about poor old Mum.

Maggie's smile faded. Poor old Mum, who they thought should be relegated to a cosy little cottage. Before she knew it they'd be arranging meals on wheels and buying her knitted bed jackets.

A flicker of anger stirred. Was that how they saw her? After all the effort she'd put into *not* being poor old Mum. Maggie
Continued overleaf

looked down at her well-cut jeans, the silk shirt and Italian shoes. She was no glamour queen, but she always made an effort and knew she did smart casual well.

Of course there were lines on her face and grey in her hair; she didn't try to hide them. But she kept herself fit and everything about her said "woman in her prime" not "old lady in a cottage".

What more did she have to do to prove it to them – get a tattoo on her shoulder?

By the time she met Alistair on Saturday, she'd viewed another couple of flats in town.

One was on the third floor of a block without a lift and, however young she felt, she knew that was not a sensible choice for the future. The second overlooked the building site for a new megastore – not the view she was hoping for.

"Grandma, this cottage is so cool!" Alistair had brought his ten-year-old daughter, who rushed into Maggie's arms for a hug. "Are you going to live here?"

"Don't get too excited, Libby," her father warned. "Grandma's not the cottage type, you know."

"But it's so much nicer than her flat."

As she walked round the property again hand in hand with her granddaughter, Maggie had to admit that it fitted the bill in many ways – a spare bedroom for when the little ones slept over and a little office fitted with the multiple sockets and phone lines needed for her computer.

"It's been modernised to a pretty high standard," was Alistair's verdict. "It's well maintained and everything's up together. I'd say it was a sound investment."

"It's so pretty," Libby said as they emerged into the garden. "You could grow lots of flowers, Grandma."

"You used to love gardening, Mum," Alistair reminded her.

"Many moons ago," Maggie quickly dismissed the memory. "It's just so…"

"What?"

"Old lady-ish."

"Hi there. It's a lovely property, isn't it?" A tall young woman had just got out of a red Mini. "And they've made a wonderful job of the modernisation." She made her way up the flower-lined path of one of the adjoining cottages.

"You… live here?" Maggie asked.

"Been here almost two years. I love it; everyone's so friendly. It's really peaceful, but you're in the city in no time – best of both worlds really. Would you like to come in and see how this one's been modernised? They all have individual features," you know."

"If you're sure you don't mind."

"Some old lady," whispered Alistair as he followed his mother up the path.

Sleepless that night, Maggie took a mental walk round the two cottages. The empty one was merely a shell; Amy's – as the young woman had introduced herself – was a home.

Fitted with modern furniture, stylish fabrics and elegant accessories, her cottage was comfortable and chic. But it was the pictures and souvenirs, knick-knacks and photographs that saved it from being merely a show house.

Maggie blinked hard and mentally hurried back to the empty cottage next door. Structurally sound, sensible layout, well-appointed kitchen, modern wiring for her computer equipment; it would suit her needs very well.

Amy had dispelled the myth that only old ladies lived in cottages, so why was she still so reluctant to make it home? What was she resisting so strongly?

"Just because it's a cottage doesn't mean I have to make it a cosy little nest."

She was surprised to find she'd spoken the words aloud.

A cosy little nest – was that what she was afraid of? That it would be much harder to make a "characterless box" out

carved. Maybe it was time to stop hiding from the past, to let the memories out of storage and create a real home again.

Eight weeks later, Maggie was completing her unpacking at Clover Cottage.

"Three boxes left, Mum." Shona placed the last one on the living room floor. "Do you want to start on them now?"

"Hmm, not sure," was Maggie's reply.

"I thought we'd found everything. You know how minimalist you are – I can't think anything's missing. What on earth's in these?"

"Memories." Maggie made her way slowly across the room, her heart pounding. "Oh well, I suppose it has to be done sometime."

Kneeling down, she wiped her clammy

Suddenly she felt very tired – of magnolia, and of keeping her memories locked away

of a pretty cottage than a flat in an anonymous block? Was she afraid that Clover Cottage might really become a home, a home with the story of her life stamped on it? A life that had known bad times as well as good, whose memories were there for all to see?

Maggie looked round at the plain magnolia walls of her bedroom, the same colour that was duplicated in every room of the flat. Suddenly she felt very tired: tired of magnolia, tired of the effort of keeping all those memories locked away.

Ten years was a long time. They had all moved on with their lives, and in truth she was content with the way things had turned out, proud of the career she had

hands on her jeans and then, taking a deep breath, she began to pull. There was a sharp ripping sound as the wide band of brown sticky tape, which had held the memories in place for over a decade, was pulled away.

A slightly sweet, musty smell rose from the crinkled cardboard packaging. Reaching in gingerly, Maggie pulled out a small package. Slowly she unravelled it.

"That's well wrapped," Shona observed. "Oh, it's so sweet!" A tiny pink porcelain pig had finally emerged.

"You gave me this one Mother's Day," Maggie told her.

"I don't remember."

Continued overleaf

Adventure

Continued from previous page

"You were only tiny and you adored pigs back then."

A tiny glass giraffe was the next treasure to be rescued from hibernation, then a little white dog with a brown patch over its ear.

"They're all so cute," Shona remarked. "Wait till Libby sees them."

"I used to have a shelf for my 'tinies'," Maggie told her. "You and Alistair always gave me something to add to it for birthdays and Christmases."

"Was it in the hall, near the window?"

"That's right."

"I remember." Shona was momentarily transported back to childhood. She and her mother knelt in bittersweet silence amid the sea of paper as the locked-away years fell away. Then they stood, and slowly Shona began to place the tiny ornaments on the mantelpiece.

"I'm sorry, darling." Maggie grasped her daughter's hand.

"Whatever for?"

"Well, it's not just my memories I've been hiding from all these years, it's yours and Alistair's, our family's memories. Memories that should be passed on to Libby and little Sam – and your children too, one day."

"They will be." Shona smiled, picking up a tiny clay mouse with a long pink tail. "Now the house won't be bare and anonymous. It's a proper home again."

Maggie felt as if a long-locked door had been unlocked to let her out into the sunshine. "My cosy little nest," she smiled.

A ring on the doorbell had them both reaching for tissues.

"Come on in," called Maggie, a little hoarsely. It was probably Amy.

"Hello?" a tentative male voice called. The women looked round as a tall man, with the kind of grey hair often described as distinguished, walked in.

Maggie registered that he was rather handsome and that he also did smart casual well, before he proffered a bouquet of yellow roses, wrapped in Cellophane.

Shona's mouth twitched into more than just a friendly smile.

"Welcome to the cottages," he said. "I'm Tom. From next door."

Smiling, Maggie held out her hand in greeting.

"Maggie. And my daughter, Shona, who's helping me unpack. Roses, how lovely, thank you." She stroked the petals.

"From the village florist, I'm afraid," Tom admitted. "I'm not really the gardening type myself."

"No roses round the door, then?" Shona asked innocently.

"'Fraid not."

"Never mind; let me find a vase."

"Now I'm in a cottage, I feel I should offer you a cup of tea and a home-baked scone," Maggie said. "But how about a glass of wine? I have some rather nice Sauvignon in the fridge."

"The new neighbour from heaven," Tom declared. "Sauvignon would be perfect."

Brain BOOSTERS

Missing Link

The answer to each clue is a word which has a link with each of the three words listed. This word may come at the end (eg **HEAD** linked with **BEACH, BIG, HAMMER**), at the beginning (eg **BLACK** linked with **BEAUTY, BOARD and JACK**) or a mixture of the two (eg **STONE** linked with **HAIL, LIME and WALL**).

ACROSS

1 Cloth, Race, Ruck (4)
3 Due, Legal, Manufacturing (7)
9 Ever, Impression, Long (7)
10 Cupboard, Handle, Stick (5)
11 Big, Political, Standard (5)
13 Being, Nature, Rights (5)
14 Board, Saw, Work (4)
16 Court, Skirt, Super (5)
18 Life, Sixth, Teacher (4)
19 Beam, Printer, Surgery (5)
21 Gun, Mentality, Under (5)
23 Case, Rod, Well (5)
24 Lawyer, Papers, Proceedings (7)
25 Call, Ear, Major (7)
26 Back, Line, Room (4)

DOWN

1 Back, Down, Proof (6)
2 Awkward, Cool, Services (8)
4 Doll, Red, Trade (3)
5 Car, Power, Stitch (5)
6 Game, Room, Willing (4)
7 Bell, Board, Sky (6)
8 Alec, Card, Move (5)
12 Board, Ice, Roller (5)
15 Background, Laboratory, Market (8)
17 Album, Raglan, Shirt (6)
18 Bite, Ground, Hoar (5)
20 Fee, Performance, Prescription (6)
21 Blood, Disease, Truth (5)
22 Country, Play, Weather (4)
24 Eyed, John, Skin (3)

Hidden word in the shaded squares: _____

The Photograph

Was there a ghost in the machine… or a guardian angel in my life? Either way, I believed wholeheartedly

By Rosie Edser

Late each afternoon, the hallway at my grandparent's house would be bathed in coloured light from the stained glass door. There was a desk to one side, filled with family pictures that sparkled in the light. Rays of colour bounced off the edges of the silver frames making the space seem like a rainbow grotto to my childish eyes.

Gran's wedding photograph stood in the centre at the back of the desk. This picture was special, though. Deep in

"Hey, Alan. See there. That's the ghost of Grandma's younger sister. She died of Spanish Flu."

"Can you die of the flu?" I'd asked, worried because my mum had had it once.

"You can die of Spanish Flu. Especially if you were on the weak side anyway."

Gran had appeared in the hallway and shooed my cousin away. She put her hand on my shoulders as I stuttered questions about a ghost appearing in the picture.

"Don't worry, love. Daisy looks over us now." She took me to the lounge and we sat as she explained that her sister used to love the woods near their house. How she

The wedding was set for a day that turned out to be six weeks after Daisy's death

the trees behind my grandparents was the face of her recently departed sister. The otherworldly face seemed to smile towards the two of them with eyes that knew the secrets of life and death.

I'd had the supernatural image pointed out to me as an eight-year-old boy. My older cousin laughed and held up the picture, eager to share his knowledge and to scare me.

was the one who cared for the family pets. How they missed her dreadfully at the wedding, which had already been set for a date that turned out to be six weeks after her death.

"I cried every day on my honeymoon as I couldn't imagine being without my sister forever. The photograph was a great comfort to me," she said. "It proved that **Continued overleaf**

Continued from previous page
Daisy still existed somewhere. And if that was true, I was sure we would meet again one day. I still am."

"So do you think that she appeared in the photograph so you would know she was at the wedding?"

"We like to think so, love – yes."

I felt an immediate connection with Daisy. As if we were linked by more than blood. I was a sensitive child, not like the other boys in my family or school. I used to feel different and my father generously put it down to me being a thinker.

Of course, being thoughtful or sensitive attracts the wrong kind of attention at school. And it was during a playground spat that Daisy guided me where to land punches on the bully who had taunted me to fight him. She seemed to draw close, even as baying classmates formed a circle round the two of us – I felt her presence.

She didn't speak or show herself. Just planted thoughts in my head. Trusting in her, I landed punch after punch, until, against the odds, I won the fight.

My friends gathered round, inspecting my cuts. "How on earth did you do that?" one boy asked.

I didn't answer truthfully. Daisy was mine. I suspected no one else had a guardian angel – or would admit to it if they did.

"You just have to focus on winning," I said instead, trembling as the adrenaline rush wore off.

Daisy set me apart from the others.

Her guidance was for me alone during my school years. She prompted me to choose study subjects that I'd overlooked. Made me forget the fact that I was a skinny, introverted teenager.

As a young married man, when I developed my own photographs in the darkroom I searched for a face in the clouds, in the lace of a curtain, and of course, in the trees.

My wife knew the family story. I delighted in finally being able to share it with another soul outside the family. I told her how Daisy had helped me. Not as a puppeteer, pulling strings, but as a guiding light in my life.

"Do you think she brought us together?" Helen asked, soon after I told her.

"No. I found you myself," I'd answered, convinced that I still held the course of life in my own hands.

After my grandfather's funeral I sat again with my grandma. We found ourselves back in the hallway, looking at the photograph once more. There were many other frames on the desk now. More weddings; children who had arrived; my cousin at his home in Australia.

"I've often felt Aunt Daisy with me, Gran," I began.

"Yes, so have I. She visits me in dreams." She picked up the photograph from the back of the display and stroked the glass. "Daisy has always loved us. I look forward to seeing her again one day. But not just yet." Her eyes shone.

She squeezed my arm and we joined the rest of the family in the lounge.

It was to be five years until Grandma joined her husband and her sister. That night, Daisy brought my grandparents to me in a dream of my own. As I slept, the

My eldest granddaughter and her husband had used every last penny of their own on fertility treatments and she would do the same with our money.

Yet that was her choice. She had as much right to choose what to do with her share as anyone else.

Daisy appeared in my thoughts.

"Remember that money is only of use in ventures that bring happiness," she whispered.

So we shared our wealth with the next two generations.

It was the following spring that Lily showed me the picture of her first scan, and there in the amniotic fluid, Daisy's face appeared to me once again.

So faint, so tiny. Probably not easily

I understood then how little we know of this life – and how much there is to come

three of them stepped out of the photograph and linked arms. They looked radiant. Younger and vibrant.

They smiled at me and I understood how little we know of this life – and how much there is to come.

There were to be years when I saw and felt no sign of her. I wondered if I had lost her, outgrown her. In my middle years it seemed that she only appeared when she was needed. A word, or a kind warning when I showed signs of doing the wrong thing.

It was long after my retirement that Daisy prompted me to gift some money to my children and grandchildren. We had more than enough after years of investments that she'd guided me to.

visible to anyone else. Yet it was so definite to me.

I felt she was saying she was going to return to us in physical form, or maybe she would watch as closely over the new baby as she had watched over me. Only time will tell. But I like to think we are going to meet in the same world for a short time at the end of my life.

And so the circle will be complete.

THE AUTHOR SAYS...

"I saw an article about early Victorian photography, where extra faces appeared in the shadows. Many were claimed as deceased relatives and I felt this would be a great comfort."

Breaking The Ice

Leaving home for the first time, Zoe quickly finds out that her new neighbours are as nice as pie…

By Christine Sutton

Zoe pulled open the freezer drawer. Her mother's conviction that a daughter leaving home would soon be existing on a diet of junk food and takeaways had seen it loaded onto the removal van with a tray of meat, a trout from Dad's last fishing trip, and three homemade pies inside.

Taking out the pies, Zoe switched on the oven. An hour later she was knocking on her neighbour's door.

"Oh, hello," she said, when it opened. "I've just moved in to…"

"Sorry," said the dark-haired man with a regretful smile, "It's Mrs Wells you want, not me. Hester," he called out, "you have another visitor."

Shame, Zoe thought as he squeezed past and walked to the lift. *I'd have liked having you as a neighbour.*

"Yes?"

She turned to find a silver-haired woman with inquisitive blue-grey eyes standing in the doorway.

"Oh, hello, Mrs Wells, I'm Zoe Lane and I just moved into the flat next door. The thing is, my freezer didn't travel too

well and I wonder if you'd mind taking this off my hands?" She held out a fresh-baked apple tart from which fragrant whorls of steam were still rising.

"My, that looks delicious," her neighbour said. "I'd love to take it, dear, if you're sure. Won't you come in and share?"

"I would, but I've got all this to offload," Zoe said, pulling back the cloth on the basket on her arm. "You could help me by telling me who's who in the building, though."

"Oh, that's easy. Directly below us is Harry Jackson. He's a schoolteacher, so he'll be out just now. And on the top floor is Adam King, the young man you just met. He helped me up with my shopping."

So he was a neighbour after all – and a kind one, at that. Zoe was just thinking she'd offer him the chicken pie when she heard a thud, thud, thud, coming from above their heads.

"Heavens, what's that?" Hester exclaimed.

"I'll go and find out," Zoe said. "Thanks, Mrs Wells. Enjoy the tart."

"Thank you, dear. I will."

Continued overleaf

Continued from previous page

Stepping from the lift, Zoe tapped on Adam King's door.

It opened to reveal him kitted out in running shorts and vest.

"Oh," she gasped, disconcerted by his muscular frame. "I'm sorry to interrupt."

"You're not," he assured her, mopping his brow with a snowy white towel. "Five minutes on that thing and I'm bored already." He nodded towards a treadmill in the middle of the lounge. That explained the thuds.

other day. I was going to offer it to Mr Jackson but…" She retrieved the fish and handed it over.

"Fantastic. I do a mean trout in pepper sauce, if you'd like to join me. Sorry, didn't catch your name?"

"Zoe Lane. I'm a paediatric nurse, just landed a job at St Joseph's."

"No way!" Adam laughed. "I'm a radiographer there, started last month."

"What a coincidence," she said. "And since I'm joining you for dinner, we can have this for dessert and run it off after with a jog in the park." She held up a

"Um, this is going to sound really cheeky but is that a trout I see in your basket?"

"But why not run outdoors?" Zoe asked, baffled. "There's a beautiful park just across the street."

"This was a gift from my mother," he said, with a wry smile. "I made the mistake of letting slip that a friend of mine had been mugged while out jogging last week. She's now convinced that the city's awash with thieves, so she ordered that thing. I've given it my best shot but breathing clean, fresh air is definitely the way to run. Anyway, how can I help?"

She explained about the freezer.

"So I wondered if you could use this?" she said, taking out the pie.

Adam peered into the basket.

"Um, this is going to sound really cheeky but is that a trout I see?"

She nodded. "Fresh caught just the

crisp lemon meringue pie.

"Sounds like a plan. Seven OK?"

She nodded. "Seven, it is."

Back in her kitchen, Zoe swiped a cloth around the freezer and closed the door. It hummed happily, as though approving of what she'd done. It wasn't quite the way Mum had intended her to use that food, but it had made the perfect ice-breaker!

• •

THE AUTHOR SAYS…

"Everyone knows how daunting moving home can be, especially for the first time. I gave my character a novel way to introduce herself to her new neighbours."

Avocado & Bacon Pancake Brunch

A tasty feast for a special occasion.

Preparation time: 15 minutes
Cooking time: 12-15 minutes

Ingredients (Makes 4)
- ✦ **110g self-raising flour**
- ✦ **Pinch of salt**
- ✦ **1 large egg**
- ✦ **4 tbsp low fat natural yogurt**
- ✦ **100ml milk**
- ✦ **Few drops of vegetable oil**
- ✦ **8 rashers streaky bacon**
- ✦ **100g Danish blue or Stilton cheese**
- ✦ **100g medium-fat soft cheese**
- ✦ **2 tbsp chopped fresh chives,**
  plus extra to garnish
- ✦ **4 tomatoes, sliced**
- ✦ **2 ripe avocados, pitted and sliced**
- ✦ **Freshly ground black pepper**

1 Put the flour, salt, egg, yogurt and milk into a mixing bowl and whisk together to make a smooth, thick batter.

2 Heat the vegetable oil in a non-stick frying pan and add tablespoons of the batter to make 8 drop scones, cooking them in batches until the batter is used up.

3 Grill the bacon until crisp. While it's cooking, mash the blue cheese with a fork and mix it with the soft cheese and chives.

4 Serve the pancakes with the tomatoes, avocados and crispy bacon, with the blue cheese mixture on the side. Sprinkle with black pepper and garnish with chives.

Cook's tip: For vegetarians, simply leave out the bacon.

RECIPE AND FOOD STYLING: SUE ASHWORTH PHOTOGRAPHY: JONATHAN SHORT

Deep Purple

As evening falls, sweet memories from a life well lived emerge one by one from the shadows…

By Jill Stitson

I'm having that dream again. The one where I'm in the park and the late evening sun is turning the trees to a deep, dreamy purple.

Roy is beside me; I can barely make out his features in the semi-darkness. And then his brown eyes come into focus as he gently lowers me to the ground where we forget everything – especially as we do not know what the next day will bring.

"She's drifting again." The voice is young and anxious and I know it is my great-granddaughter, Chloe.

I open my eyes and smile at her, squeezing the soft hand clasping mine. I want to tell her not to worry; I have had a full and wonderful life and I'm not afraid, but I'm too tired to speak.

I see a trace of Roy in the dark eyes and the creamy skin, and then I let myself go and am back in the mists of memory.

Roy and I are walking hand in hand in Bushy Park. He is very handsome in his uniform and it's spring. The horse chestnuts and limes are in bud and there is the sweet smell of lavender. We reach Diana's Fountain and survey the statue.

"She's not as pretty as you, honey."

Roy's voice is dark and soft with desire and by unspoken agreement we wander off into the shelter of the trees. Then I drift again until I hear my mother.

"How could you! How could you! What about the *neighbours*?" Her voice trails off and I answer defiantly.

"We're getting married and he's the most wonderful man on earth!"

Of course, it didn't work out like that. Roy was killed during the D-Day landings. He had been one of the thousands of Americans based in Bushy Park near Hampton Court. We met at a dance and jitterbugged like crazy, fallen for each other and made love in the shadows of the deep purple trees, cushioned by the soft moss.

"How are you, Mum?"

Competent hands smooth my hair and bathe my forehead with lavender water. My daughter, Pauline, is leaning over me and I smile at her, remembering the little girl with dark skin and tight black curls, born before Roy and I could marry.

Amazingly, my mother had fallen in love with Pauline the moment she saw her and so our path had not been so rough.

Continued overleaf

Continued from previous page

She looked after her while I went back to work and tried to pick up the pieces of what I had thought to be a broken heart.

When you are young, the heart has a way of mending and I met John, a quiet, kind man who became my best friend before I realised I loved him. We married, John accepting Pauline as if she were his. We also had two children of our own and Pauline was a lovely big sister to them.

"Shall, I sing to you, Mum?" Pauline sings a soft, plaintive ballad which soothes me as I slip once more into the past.

Pauline was a wild child of the swinging Sixties with a wonderful voice. She sang at gigs in Richmond and Eel Pie Island with a pop group that almost, but not quite, made it to the top.

When she returned to live with us, we discovered she had had a little boy, Andy. John and I had welcomed her and looked after him. Pauline had never married, but remained independent and amazed us by becoming a nurse, although singing was her joy.

Our own two children did marry and before I knew it, I was grandmother to six.

"Gran, it's me, Andy." I open my eyes and look at the middle-aged man beside me; my first grandson, Pauline's child. The dark eyes are full of concern. I want to say everything is fine. I am where I want to be.

"She's fine, Andy." Pauline's calm voice reassures. "Tell her about Chloe."

My eyes go back to Andy and he tells me that Chloe, his daughter, Roy's and my great-grandchild, has made it into the big time of London's theatre-land. She has a role in the latest musical, singing and dancing in the chorus. It's a start, he says. She's still very young.

Of course she is, I think. I was young like that once and I'm back in time with John. He worked so hard to give us all a loving and comfortable home, and what good times and holidays we had. I can feel the hot, stony beach of Brighton beneath my feet, then the soft sands of Bournemouth and sandcastles.

Once at a tea dance we swayed sedately to a waltz – a far cry from jitterbugging with Roy, but just as sweet.

Later, when the children left home, John had taken me to Spain and France and it was once more just the two of us, comfortable together. Oh, how I missed him when he went before me, but there were always children to be cherished.

It seems to be growing darker.

"I can't bear it!" Chloe's voice again

"Shush!" This from Pauline. "You will bear it and you will be brave, just as she has always been."

Then all the others come. I feel kisses on my cheek. The room is filled with love.

The light appears gradually and I feel perfectly content. Roy's voice first and then John's. I smell lavender and feel the firm touch of John's hand. It is time.

• •

THE AUTHOR SAYS...

"I was born near Bushy Park. Americans were based there during and after the war, and I recall two girls in 'my road' becoming pregnant by them."

FANCY THAT!

"Babe" was played by more than 50 piglets

Fascinating facts for **fluffy girls!**

◆ If a squirrel finds a baby squirrel without parents, it will immediately adopt it.

◆ **A group of pugs is called a grumble.**

◆ As if a group of Pomeranians isn't cute enough, a duo is called a "puff" and a group of three or more is called a "tuft"

◆ **Cuddling releases oxytocin, which improves mood, fights depression and aids healing.**

A group of rabbits is called a "Fluffle" – too adorable!

◆ In Sweden they have a bunny jumping show called "Kaninhoppming"!

◆ Japanese Macaque monkeys have worked out how to use coins they find to get food from vending machines.

◆ A group of cats are a clowder, pounce or glaring; a group of kittens are a litter or a kindle.

WORDS: BABS BEATON PICTURES: ISTOCKPHOTO.REX/SHUTTERSTOCK

Orphan Girl

It was time for Isabella to make her way in the world –
holding fast to her her slender hope of finding love

By Pauline Saull

ILLUSTRATIONS: REX/SHUTTERSTOCK, ISTOCKPHOTO, JOHN BARRIE

September the fourteenth, 1851, was Isabella Hornchurch's eighteenth birthday. Time for her to leave the place she considered home, her haven – St Paul's Orphanage, thirty-two, Willow Street, Brisbane, where she had lived since she was five.

Matron Shilling spoke kindly to her. "It's sad that we have to find other homes for our children when they come of age, but we desperately need the room for younger orphans. You will be well cared for, Isabella. The Wilsons are good people, and who knows, you may even meet a young man once you are living with a family who entertain. You are far too pretty to stay on the shelf for long!"

Isabella sighed quietly, and not wishing to upset Matron, nodded.

"Your duties will be light, dear. Mrs Wilson, as you know, is very impressed with your needlework. She regularly sends fine linens to her family in England, especially when exquisitely embroidered, so you will be kept busy."

And so Isabella settled into life at the Wilson home in a leafy suburb of Brisbane. As Matron Shilling had said, the Wilsons were extremely kind; she was treated well, had her own room and two half-days a week off. She ate her meals in the downstairs kitchen with Cook and the housemaid, Rosie, and spent a lot of time on her needlework, which she loved.

Drawn threadwork, silk embroidery and smocking came easily to her, as did the making of dresses. On their days off she and Rosie loved to wonder around the shops, giggling as they imagined themselves decked out in the finery displayed in windows.

Isabella had no real desire for fancy clothes or hats; what she wanted more than anything was a fine young man to marry, with hopefully the blessing of children. Yet she knew this was hardly likely to happen.

"Do you think you'll ever wed?" Rosie asked her one day. They were having breakfast together and Rosie idly played with one of Isabella's long golden ringlets.

"I don't know, Rosie. Though I do know it would have to be to a caring, kind man, one I wanted to marry. What about you and that handsome gardener?"

Continued overleaf

Rosie giggled shyly. "I think he's lovely. Perhaps one day…"

Cook looked up from pounding her bread dough.

"If you have any sense stay single, the pair of you, that's my advice," she said, and gave the dough an extra thump.

Isabella glanced at Rosie, amusement gone, for both were aware of Cook's errant husband who had left without a word seven years ago. Isabella looked at Cook's pinched face and felt a pang of sadness. She rose from the table.

"Let me do that for you," she said.

In the thriving hill town of Malkenny, Cal Harris stood back to survey the finishing touches being put to his hotel.

"It's a grand building, Cal." Reverend and Mrs Stuart had stopped with other townspeople to watch the erecting of the sign above the wide front porch. *Traveller's Rest*, it said in beautifully painted writing. "You've done well."

"I'm pleased with it." Cal Harris's blue eyes glittered with pride, for the building was indeed fine. Two storeys with ornate fretwork railings around the verandas, wide windows and doors, and inside, tasteful furnishings.

"I hear," Mrs Stuart said, "that you already have all the rooms booked for the holidays. My, what an achievement. I do think," she added, leaning forward with a smile, "that it is time you found a bride, Callum Harris.

"All this building and making fortunes! What good is it to you without a wife and family to enjoy it with? Look at all these girls! Any one of them would be glad to be seen on your arm."

Cal scratched his chin.

"Well, you know, Mrs Stuart, maybe I'm just too darn picky!"

"Oh! How is that?"

"All the girls I meet seem interested only in the latest fashions, the way a fellow wears his hat, his hairstyle, fancy shoes. That's not for me." He sighed, looking around the small crowd, at the girls in their pretty dresses. "Though where I'll find what I really want, I don't know."

"Mm." Mrs Stuart looked at him. "Have you considered writing to one of the orphanages?"

Cal looked shocked.

"No. What would I want an orphan for?"

"Callum, dear. When girls reach eighteen they must leave the orphanage. They've been well-educated, well brought up and nearly always have the most charming manners. They usually end up as housemaids. I have had some experience in this matter. Trust me, dear. Many would rather make a good marriage than a good housemaid!"

"I couldn't do that," Callum said firmly. "There's something – I dunno…"

Mrs Stuart shook her head.

"I can assure you, it is totally respectable. And I could make enquiries for you. Matron Shilling of St Paul's in Brisbane is an old friend of mine."

"Let me think about it."

That evening Callum sat outside on the porch of his home on the outskirts of town and gazed across his acres of land.

Yes, he thought, *I would like a wife and children. Mrs Stuart is right. It's fine having all this, but it would be much better to have someone I loved to share it with.*

"Maybe," he murmured thoughtfully, "I should do as she suggested."

And so it was that the letter landed on Matron Shilling's desk from her friend Mavis Stuart in Kilcanny, enquiring if she knew of any suitable girls who might be interested in meeting a charming and personable young man.

Matron Shilling straight away thought of Isabella. Taking out her pen, she dipped it in the inkwell and began writing.

Dear Isabella,

Thank you for your last letter. I am man, *whom she assures me is from a good background, and has exceptional manners. His name is Callum Harris, he is twenty-seven, lives on a small holding on the outskirts of Kilcanny, and is anxious to meet a young woman of a similar background with a view to an eventual marriage… should that suit both parties, of course. To me, you would appear to be the ideal person, but you would have to meet him and make your own choice.*

Think about it, Isabella. Show this letter to the Wilsons and ask their advice.

I look forward to hearing from you.

Fond regards,

Matron Shilling

Isabella read the letter twice, puzzled, intrigued, and with a fair amount of interest. By all accounts Callum Harris

He is from a good background, lives on a small holding and has exceptional manners

pleased you have settled in well, I was always sure you would.

Now, I have news for you. I received a letter from an old friend of mine, wife to a minister in a small country town, who is making enquiries on behalf of a young sounded a serious-minded young man. She gazed out of the window onto the busy street where carriages clattered by.

A small holding!

Her heart rate quickened slightly, imagining chickens, maybe a goat, or perhaps a cow, a place where there was room for her to grow vegetables; fresh, clean country air.

"Callum Harris," she murmured.

She was still smiling, the letter in her hand when Mrs Wilson arrived home.

"You look happy, Isabella. Good news?"

"I'm not sure. It came from the Matron at the orphanage. She suggests I ask your advice." Isabella passed the letter over.

Continued overleaf

Continued from previous page

Mrs Wilson read it thoughtfully before passing it back. Her eyes glowed.

"I think it sounds an excellent idea! I have heard of this happening before many times. Young men disillusioned with the modern misses of today who want a lady with… a little class, shall we say, regularly approach the orphanages.

"I will speak to my husband about it over dinner, but I think you should consider meeting him, Isabella. No one will compel you do anything you do not wish to do. Indeed, I should be very sad to lose you, but Robert and I have often said that it is a crime you are not settled down with a good young man."

Five weeks later, Isabella sat waiting in the drawing room. The meeting was arranged for eleven thirty, and she glanced at the grandfather clock every few minutes.

Rosie had been instructed by Mrs Wilson to place a tray of cool lemonade and two of the best crystal glasses on the side table, and had insisted on buying yards of yellow-sprigged muslin out of which Isabella had made herself a dress.

She smoothed the skirt and glanced at the clock again. Three minutes to go.

Mrs Wilson popped her head around the door and smiled.

"We'll be on the veranda," she said. "I think I have just heard a carriage. Good luck, my dear."

Isabella heard Rosie's little feet pitter-patter down the polished hallway accompanied by the sound of a wide stride. She clenched her hands in her lap. Her pulse beat rapidly in anticipation.

The door opened and Rosie, wide-eyed, mouth agape, managed to say, "Your visitor, Miss," as she pushed the door open for Callum Harris to enter.

"Thank you, Rosie, that will be all," Isabella said as calmly as she could. She rose. "Mr Harris, please take a seat."

My word! she thought.

It was hard to take her eyes off him. Tall, with thick black hair, he had the bluest eyes she had ever seen.

But… I must remain cool-headed, she reminded herself. *His is a serious mission, and I have a serious question to ask of him.*

"Yes, please, that would be most welcome, Miss Hornchurch."

"Mr Harris." Isabella took a deep breath. "I will not beat about the bush as that is not my way. You have asked for a meeting with an eventual aim which I regard as quite serious. If we are to converse freely, I would like you to call me Isabella, and I shall address you as Callum." She smiled shyly. "Does my forwardness shock you?"

Callum smiled, enchanted by the stunning young woman.

"No, it does not, but I would rather call it forthrightness – a trait I admire greatly. And you are quite right. This is a serious matter. You see… Isabella, meeting suitable young ladies is, for us men, usually organised by over-zealous mothers!"

Isabella laughed softly.

"Ah. And yours is like this too?"

Callum felt himself relaxing, though perspiration still trickled down his back.

She really is beautiful, he thought.

"No, my mother is Irish… hence my name, and believes men and women should have the freedom to choose a life partner for themselves."

Isabella nodded and bit her lip before saying, "Only one thing concerns me about your – quest, shall we call it? And that is the fact that you approached the orphanage. Please do not take this the wrong way but I have to ask…"

"Please, Isabella, ask anything of me."

All I want to do, Callum thought, *is reach across and hold her!*

"Well, I shall say it then. I wonder if because orphans are considered so badly done by, people believe we will grasp at the first opportunity that comes along, and once wed will willingly become an unpaid servant?"

Callum stared at her, horrified, mortified. He opened his mouth but nothing came out. He tugged at the collar of his crisp white shirt and pulled the cravat loose.

"Isabella, please believe me, I had no such thoughts. I promise you I would never expect any woman to be a servant to me. Mrs Stuart encouraged me, you see, and I, well, I …"

His voice trailed off and he looked at her helplessly.

She is everything I could ever have hoped for and I have lost her already, he thought miserably.

Isabella watched the helplessness, the confusion and hurt twist his handsome face and her heart seemed to perform a little flip in her chest.

I have hurt him, she thought. *How unforgiveble.* Without any hesitation, reaching across, she placed her hand on his and felt it tremble.

"I'm sorry to have upset you with my question, Callum, but I felt it was one I had to ask… to be sure, you see." She looked down at her small, pale hand lying upon his tanned, slender one and experienced a jolt of pleasure as he placed his other gently over the top of it.

"Isabella," he said softly and something inside her melted.

They looked at each other, eyes locked, and for Isabella no further words were needed at that moment.

There would, she felt sure, be many more meetings between them when a deep friendship and love would develop.

Each had a great deal to learn about the other, and maybe subsequent encounters would prove to be equally important as this one today – but today's would shine especially bright in her memory for she had, with a great rush of happiness and hope, silently made her decision.

I have given you my heart, Callum.

THE AUTHOR SAYS...

"In the early 20th Century, I believe some orphanages in Canada endeavoured to find suitable husbands for their young women of marriageable age. This sparked the idea for my story of Isabella."

The Recipe For Love

Life is so frustrating for a devoted daughter, kitchen maid and unacknowledged culinary genius…

By Christine Sutton

Izzie pushed her fingers into the dough, kneading firmly. The Master would be down soon for his breakfast and with Mrs Lang still unwell, there was precious little time to get everything ready.

Behind her, the kettle began to sing as the contents came to the boil. Wiping her hands on a cloth, she folded it and wrapped it around the handle, ready to fill up the teapot.

"Izzie," barked a voice just as she was lifting it, "where's my bread dough?"

She jerked round to see Cook glaring at her from the doorway. Relief at the thought that she was no longer alone was tempered by a feeling of trepidation. All week her irascible superior had been laid low with a stomach upset – due, Izzie suspected, to a somewhat lackadaisical approach to hygiene. Now she was back and clearly feeling no sunnier of nature, despite her enforced rest.

As scalding water slopped from the spout onto Izzie's bare arm she sucked in her breath. Biting back the unladylike oath that sprang to her lips, she replaced the kettle on the hob.

"It's just coming, Mrs Lang," she answered, noting that proprietorial "my". This habit of Cook's of taking credit for everything that left the kitchen, no matter who had prepared it, was beginning to pall.

Grumbling about it to her sweetheart, Samuel, just the other day, she'd been not a little put out when he'd appeared to take the older woman's side.

"It must be hard for her, Isabella, childless as she is," he'd said, as they strolled by the Thames one evening after work. "You are not yet a mother but have been caring for your siblings for so long your experience far outstrips hers.

"As your senior, she must feel that keenly. Nevertheless, if you feel yourself ill-used, then we must think of a way to claim your skills as your own."

"And how do you propose we do that?" she'd asked, reluctant to forgive him too quickly for having the temerity to see the other's point of view.

"That I have yet to decide but I will put my mind to it. Give me time," he'd said.

Izzie sighed. Time, always more time.

She turned her attention back to the dough. It would need to prove before baking, something Mrs Lang liked to preside over personally, as though the workings of yeast and sugar were **Continued overleaf**

Green Peas

Artichokes.

Tomatoes.

Potatoes

Spanish Onions

Salad

Vegetable Marrow

Broad Beans.

Cauliflowers.

Asparagus.

Sea Kale.

Carrots.

Brussels Sprouts

French Beans

somehow enhanced by her nearness. She carried the bowl over to where Cook had started chopping boiled eggs for the Master's kedgeree.

"Hmph," grumped the older woman, giving the bowl a cursory glance. "I trust you have added no 'extras' this time. No bits of tree bark, or crushed shell."

Izzie curbed the temptation to tell the woman not to be so silly. Left to her own devices she had experimented by mixing some honey and cinnamon-spiced apple into the dough for yesterday's breakfast rolls. The result had been light, sweet rolls that melted in the mouth. The glow she'd felt when Jenny brought the tray back devoid of so much as a crumb with the

Izzie bit back a smile as irrepressible housemaid Jenny breezed in, a metal pan of powdery grey ashes from the dining room hearth held out before her.

The girls had both been taken on at the same time, following the death of Mrs Barton a little over a year ago. Left with a large house to run and no idea how to do it, the Master had straight away increased his staff by two. Only Cook and Snell, the butler, lived in, the girls preferring accommodation outside.

"Never off duty, else," Jenny had told her. "Think they can have you at their beck and call all night too."

She had a point, although Izzie had no choice in the matter of where she lived. Her father's early demise when she was

"I am barely twenty years old. What woman will take advice from a chit of a girl?"

message that Mr Burton had much enjoyed the new recipe and would like them that way again, please, had lasted all day. Judging by this mealy-mouthed comment, though, Mrs Lang had heard of it and taken a dim view of her underling's small triumph.

"No, ma'am," she said, with as much meekness as she could muster, "no more than flour, yeast, sugar, water and milk."

Cook nodded. "So I should think. Good, plain food, that's what Mr Burton likes, none of your fancy nonsense. Now go and get that tea made, girl. Can't think what you've been doing all this time."

"I can tell you that," said a perky voice from across the room. "She's been boiling eggs, making dough, poaching haddock and scouring pots."

just a child had left her mother with a large family to bring up alone. As the eldest, Isabella was much called upon to help. She did so willingly, but with such demands on her time she'd convinced herself that no man would ever want her.

Then she'd met Samuel, a well respected publisher and son of her mother's best friend. Far from being put off by her devotion he seemed genuinely touched by it and they had been walking out for several months.

Today being her half-day, she would see him this afternoon. Her heart gave a little leap at the prospect. Perhaps today would be the day when he finally decided that their courtship had gone on long enough and it was time to ask that special question she longed to answer…

The morning passed in a whirl of preparation for the Master's evening meal and before she knew it, the clock was striking one. Cook looked up at it and scowled.

"I suppose you'll be wanting to get off home now."

Izzie suppressed the urge to point out that with the woman confined to her bed most of the week, she'd had to work seven days non-stop, saying instead, "If convenient to you, ma'am. My young man will be waiting for me."

To her great surprise, the older woman's face softened and a flush of pink tinged her crinkly cheeks.

"Ah, is that the way of it? Well, far be it from me to stand in the way of young love. Off you go now."

Feeling slightly bewildered, Izzie donned her cape and stepped out into the sunshine. There was Samuel, waving from the entrance to the park. How handsome he looked in his grey tailcoat and top hat. A brief pause to let a horse-drawn carriage pass and she raised her skirts and hurried across the street.

"You look happier today, my love," he said, capturing her hand and pressing it to his lips. "Has something happened?"

"In a way," she said, thinking of Mrs Lang's unexpected warmth. "Yesterday I baked the breakfast rolls to my own recipe, which the Master said he much enjoyed. I felt so proud. Then, a moment ago, Cook actually raised a smile and wished me a lovely afternoon. It made me think that perhaps she isn't such a harridan after all."

He smiled. "I'm glad. Perhaps this problem of yours is not so pressing now?"

She shook her head, thinking of that barbed remark about the rolls. "Oh, I doubt very much that her change of heart will extend to letting me take the credit for my own efforts. There are limits!"

He chuckled. "You may be right. Well, I have given the matter much thought and I believe that the answer is for you to write a series of articles that I will publish in my magazine."

"Articles," Izzie echoed, "about what?"

"All the things you know most about, my dear, like cookery, needlework, and child care," he said.

She wrinkled her brow.

"Still, I am barely twenty years old, Samuel. What woman is going to take advice on such important things from a chit of a girl – and an unmarried one, at that?"

"You make a very good point," he said seriously. "So…" Taking a small red box from his pocket, he lifted the lid. "Miss Isabella Mayson, would you do me the very great honour of becoming my wife?"

Izzie's eyes grew round. She looked up at him, breathless with happiness.

"Oh, Samuel, yes, I will marry you. And you are right, *Mrs Beeton's Book of Household Management* does have a much better ring to it!"

. . . .

THE AUTHOR SAYS…

"A TV item about Isabella's famous book had me wondering how she had learned her housekeeping skills so young. Researching her life led me to write this story."

Up In The Gallery

There's always one punter who takes things too literally – but seasoned performer Marie can handle it

By Donald Lightwood

You could feel the audience's anticipation as Marie Lloyd reached the last song in her act.

It had made her famous and placed her at the top of the bill in all of London's music halls. Everybody knew the words.

The boy I love is up in the gallery, the boy I love is looking now at me...

As you would expect, she directed the words up to the theatre gallery. *There he*

"That mean I'm due a rise, then?" she returned smartly.

He laughed. "Always the comic," he told her, re-folding the paper.

There was a large headline on the front page. *WAR DECLARED.*

As a top ranking artist, Marie Lloyd had her own dressing room. She cherished this mark of her success more than anything else. She'd been in the business for over thirty years and she'd

The young man clutched at his cap and swallowed. "I'm the boy you love," he said.

is, can't you see... prompting the men to respond as she sang. *Waving his handkerchief...*

She was exhausted when she finally came off the stage after the inevitable encore. The Pavilion's manager met her in the wings. He was holding a newspaper.

"Did you see the Standard, Marie?" he asked her.

"Can't say I did."

He had the paper open at the show page.

"1914's been our best year yet," he declared. "Thanks to our own dear Marie."

had to share for many of them.

She opened the first of two bottles of stout. This was medicinal, for her throbbing vocal cords. The second, she told herself, was her reward for all her hard work on the boards.

There was a knock on the door.

"Come in, if you're sober!" she called.

The door opened slowly, revealing a young man clutching his cap in his hands.

"Who are you, then?" Marie asked.

He stared at her open-mouthed.

Continued overleaf

"Well?" She took a swig of stout.

The young man swallowed and made himself speak.

"I'm the boy you love," he said.

"You what?"

"Up in the gallery."

She snorted, spilling some stout.

"That's a good one, that is. What you really here for?"

He hesitated, twisting his cap. "I come every night and you always point at me."

"Don't be daft," she told him. "I point at all the lads up there."

"No you don't. I'm always in the same seat and you always pick me out."

"I can't even see you when I'm on the stage." She topped up her glass, concentrating on it, rather than him.

"No, you don't. You've fallen in love with the woman I pretend to be. Like all the other blokes."

He stood in silence, the look on his face reminding her of her dog when she wouldn't take him out.

She went on. "It's the name of the game – music hall, the theatre, all of it. Illusion. We're a dream factory."

"I know that," he said.

"Well, then."

"I'm different."

"It doesn't sound like it to me," she replied tartly.

"I've lost count how many times I've seen you," he said. "I know I love you."

She shook her head, irritated, and pointed at the greasepaint and powder on her dressing table.

"You need specs, duck. And I'll tell you something else; I am not a good woman"

"I can see you," he said.

"'Course you can," she retorted. "That's what it's all about."

He edged a little further into the room. Marie sat up in her chair, on her guard.

"You're the only girl I've ever loved," he told her breathlessly.

She gave out a yelp.

"Girl! Blimey, that's a good one, that is." She laughed out loud. "Want a bet? I bet I'm old enough to be your mother."

"I don't care."

"How old are you?"

"Nineteen."

"I was right," she cried. "I could have had you and half a dozen more."

"I still love you," he protested.

She took off the flowered headdress she always wore on stage.

"See them? They're my tools. Without them I'd be nothing." She looked in the mirror. "See that pretty face? I'll show you what's under it."

She spread removing cream on her face and rubbed it off thoroughly with a towel. The evocative smell of greasepaint filled the room.

"See – the old battleaxe."

Naturally, being Marie, she exaggerated. For a forty-four-year-old woman her face was a little worn, but still acceptable.

"You're still lovely," he said.

"You need specs, duck," she replied, peering at herself in the mirror. "I'll tell you something else. I am not a good woman. I've been divorced, lived in sin, and I drink too much. The lot." She stopped and turned sharply to face him. "Why am I telling you all this anyway?"

A slight smile had crept onto his face.

She glanced away, but could still see his reflection in the mirror. In her mind she answered her own question.

Because it can't go on forever. Pretending to be the cheeky fresh-faced young girl who had won audiences over the years. She'd become two people.

Seemingly the magic still worked. But for how much longer?

"How did you get in here, anyway?" she demanded.

"I waited till the others had gone and the doorkeeper was stuck in his newspaper."

"You'd better go." She shook out her hair. "This is supposed to be my happy time, not making my confession."

He handed her a picture postcard from his pocket.

"Will you sign this for me, please?"

"Stone the crows," she said, looking at an early photograph of herself. "That's me, about your age."

"It's beautiful."

She smiled. "That girl really had something. What's your name?"

He gasped when he read what she had written.

To Alfred, with much love from Marie. I won't forget you.

She held up her hand.

"Before you get carried away, that's from her up on the stage," she told him firmly. "Understood?"

He nodded and put on his cap.

"I think I'll go now, Marie."

"Yes, I think you should, Alfred."

After the show a few days later, Marie was on her second bottle of stout when the manager came into her dressing room.

"Sorry about the rumpus in the gallery after your last number," he told her.

"What was the trouble?" she asked.

"You, in a way." He grinned. "It seems one of the punters was boasting about how you'd told him you loved him. He'd had a drink, of course. Anyway some of the lads decided to sort him out."

"Men," she said, pulling a face. "I thought he was a bit different. Ah well. Nothing changes."

"That's where you're wrong, my dear."

Continued overleaf

Continued from previous page

He dropped a piece of sheet music on to the dressing table.

"What's this?"

"A new number – and you'll be doing it all this week."

"Hang on," she protested. "I'm the one who chooses what I sing."

"Not when General Kitchener's about, you don't," he told her. "It's Marie Lloyd's contribution to the War Effort."

The Pavilion Theatre was decked out in red, white and blue bunting for the following night's performance. After she'd sung her last number, Marie was joined on stage by the company waving flags and a recruiting sergeant.

"This song is specially for all the young chaps here tonight," cried Marie. Her patriotic words filled the house.

We don't want to lose you,
But we think you ought to go.
Your King and Country
Both need you so.

The audience cheered and after am encore, the recruiting sergeant spoke up.

"Now lads, you heard what the lady said, and she's dead right. Step up here and take the King's Shilling – and you'll get a kiss from the lovely Marie Lloyd."

The band played and men were urged forward by their wives and sweethearts. A queue of volunteers formed rapidly down the aisle and up onto the stage.

Marie dutifully kissed the young men, who mostly appeared to be struck dumb with the emotion of the moment.

There was one exception. Alfred. He stood beaming in front of Marie with a black eye. She couldn't help a giggle.

"I still love you, Marie," he said.

"'Course you do, ducks."

"No, I mean it," he went on. "You changed my life. I was nobody – but now I'm somebody."

"Come on, give us a kiss," she said. "My hero," she told him as they parted.

His eyes shone. "Honest?"

"I haven't never had no blokes have a scrap over me before."

"Get moving there!" shouted the sergeant. "We got a war to win."

"I love both of you," Alfred called over his shoulder as he marched away.

She gave him a fond smile and then faced up to the next star-struck volunteer, prepared to do her duty.

• • • • • • • • • • • • • • • • • • • •

THE AUTHOR SAYS...

"Marie Lloyd did perform at the Pavilion Theatre in August 1914, aged 44. See how the music hall helped recruitment in the film *Oh What A Lovely War*."

FANCY THAT!

Fascinating facts for **worldly girls!**

✦ The voice of Mickey Mouse and the voice of Minnie Mouse got married in real life.

✦ In one decade from 1989, 10million lbs of glitter has been purchased.

✦ **There is enough gold in the Earth's core to cover the entire surface of the planet with 1.5 feet of it!**

✦ The largest flower in the world is called Rafflesia Arnoldii. It can grow as big as an umbrella and smells like decaying flesh.

✦ **Women have been shown to only argue with those they care about. If they're not interested in you they can't be bothered to argue with you!**

✦ Blind people smile – even though they've never seen anyone else smile.

✦ **Cows produce more milk when they listen to soft, soothing music.**

THE NORTH POLE

✦ **You can always see your own nose – your brain simply chooses to ignore it.**

Earth's magnetic north pole is moving northward at the rate of 10 miles per year

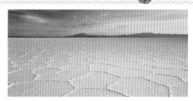

✦ The Salar de Uyuni is the largest salt flat in the world and so reflective it perfectly mirrors the sky, creating amazing dream-like landscapes.

WORDS: BABS BEATON PICTURES: ISTOCKPHOTO, ALAMY

The Voyage

We were all eager to embark for America. But would little Emily recover from her fever in time?

by Hazel E. Kendrick

Monday 1st April, 1912

All Fools Day, but my boisterous sons, William and Albert cannot play noisy tricks. Their sister Emily is ill.

Not serious, our doctor assures me. Dear Ernest says I worry over-much.

He is anticipating our voyage. This trip to America will encourage his business prosperity. I have not journeyed with him for some while, but now the boys are older Emily rising four, I felt I could travel and bookings were made.

This is the first entry in my journal for days, such has been my preoccupation. Soon Ernest will come home, hurrying to the nursery the moment Jenkins has taken his hat.

Emily is our treasure. Our youngest child. Should we lose her, life would be unbearable and difficult to contemplate.

Thursday 4th April, 1912

We are due to sail on the 10th April. I have requested Jenkins to have the trunk brought down from the attics. My maid, Clara, is accompanying us and is busy pressing my finest gowns.

The idea of the voyage has caused Clara, who has never before left her native land, to become quite giddy! However poor dear Emily still tosses restlessly.

Ernest says little. A man of good breeding, he has not been brought up to show emotion.

Saturday 6th April, 1912

The doctor has visited twice. Fear is renewed. Emily's temperature has risen. I am distraught.

I agonise over whether I should still accompany my husband on the voyage. There are but four days to departure.

Ernest has tried to reassure me. A trained nurse is already engaged, the doctor is optimistic. Ernest has pointed out that with new Marconigrams we may be in touch, even though miles distant.

Still I am torn. How can I be far from land, unable to rush to her side if Emily begins struggling for survival?

Monday 9th April, 1912

My decision is made. I cannot travel. Clara shows bitter disappointment, weeping copiously as she replaced my splendid gowns in wraps.

She is but a girl of seventeen summers. I could not be angry – may Clara never know the sharp pain of anxiety that dwells in this mother's heart.

Tonight at dinner, Ernest declared that **Continued overleaf**

Continued from previous page

he has cancelled all three passages.

My dearest Ernest. The trip meant so much to him. Its postponement may delay the growth of his business.

However, he is quite determined. That he could love his family so much, put us before all else, brings much comfort.

Wednesday 11th April, 1912

The doctor has said a turning point draws near and has warned I must take rest to retain my strength. Instead, I write this journal.

Clara tells me wistfully that the newspapers showed photographs of our liner's departure from port. I murmur to Clara that there will be other opportunities.

Sunday 14th April, 1912

Praise be. Emily's fever has broken, all is well. Today her mischievous smile dimpled. She asked for bread and milk and I ran to the kitchens myself to fetch it, to the astonishment of Cook.

Ernest has been my strength, constant with gentle words and warm enfolding arms. When I ventured regrets on the failure of the business opportunity, he held me close.

"There will be other opportunities, Maud," he murmured, just as I had told Clara. "Family life is precious."

Wednesday 17th April, 1912

Nanny Hawkins has administered smelling salts for faintness to Clara. There has been news of an immense disaster. The liner on which we were to travel, the beautiful S.S. Titanic on her maiden voyage, has foundered.

She struck an iceberg on the 15th April in this year of our Lord, 1912. Rumours abound of large loss of life, which are then contradicted.

Few details are yet known, but I feel a dread chill as though I had sunk into the icy depths myself.

As is customary, doubtless women and children were taken off first. Had I travelled with Ernest, could I have left him on that stricken ship awaiting rescue?

God has spared me that horrendous decision because we chose to stay with Emily. Clara is safe, too.

Even as I pray for the lost souls, I give thanks for Ernest and his appreciation of the meaning of precious family ties.

THE AUTHOR SAYS...

"I have always been fascinated by the tragic story of The Titanic and began wondering how a grand lady of that era might feel, had she been spared like Maud."

Peach & Amaretto Pancakes

This delicious dessert is indulgent yet light.
Preparation time: 15 minutes
Cooking time: 12 minutes

Ingredients (Makes 4)
+ **3 peaches, pitted and sliced**
+ **50g caster sugar**
+ **4tbsp Amaretto liqueur**
+ **Shredded zest and juice of 1 orange**
+ **110g plain flour**
+ **Pinch of salt**
+ **1 large egg**
+ **200ml milk**
+ **A few drops of vegetable oil**
+ **Whipped double cream and toasted flaked almonds, to decorate**

1 Put the peach slices into a shallow pan with the sugar, liqueur, orange zest, orange juice and 2tbsp water. Simmer gently for 4-5min, until tender.

2 Meanwhile, make the pancakes. Put the flour, salt, egg and milk into a mixing bowl and whisk them together until a smooth batter is formed.

3 Heat a few drops of vegetable oil in a pancake pan. Pour in a quarter of the batter, cook over a medium heat until set, then flip over to cook the other side.
Cook 4 pancakes like this, keeping them covered in a warm place (such as a low oven) until they are all cooked.

4 Serve the pancakes and peaches with whipped cream, scattered with a few flaked almonds.

Cook's tip: If you'd rather not use alcohol, then simply replace the liqueur with the juice of another orange.

RECIPE AND FOOD STYLING: SUE ASHWORTH · PHOTOGRAPHY: JONATHAN SHORT

Freedom For Fortunata

Life was harsh as a slave of the Romans – but the consequences of a failed escape would be worse…

By Dawn Knox

P lease reconsider, mistress! I humbly beg you!"

"Fortunata! You're my slave, not my mother. Stop fussing! It's all worked out. I'll go to the feast and then excuse myself with a headache.

"No one will give me a second thought, especially my parents. Tomorrow night's about impressing the governor and all the other stuffy dignitaries who've been invited. They'll talk boring politics all evening.

"But once I've gone to my room, you can smuggle Felix in and then stand guard. Everyone'll be happy. But I need you to get a message to him while you're out on your errands this morning."

As Horatia absent-mindedly held the mouth of a tiny alabaster jar to her wrist allowing the exotic perfume to dribble on to her skin, tiny drops of oil trickled unnoticed on to her lap. Fortunata sighed.

When Horatia noticed the spots on her tunic, she would demand it be taken to the fuller's to be cleaned. Highly-prized while in the alabaster jar or when stroked across the skin, the expensive perfume would

suddenly become undesirable when it revealed itself as a stain on the snowy fabric. A case of being in the wrong place at the wrong time.

Fortunata knew all about that. She'd been the daughter of an important man, but that had counted for nothing when the Romans conquered her city and carried her back to Rome as a slave. How ironic that the price of the tiny jar of scented oil was more than Horatia's mother had paid for Fortunata at the slave market.

Despite the name Fortunata, there was nothing fortunate about her life. Her wealthy Roman master, Quintus, and his wife, Claudia, were an imposing couple; both tall and elegant but each had a quick temper and Claudia, in particular, had a vindictive streak, which Horatia, her pampered daughter, had inherited.

Negotiations for the betrothal of Horatia to the son of a Roman senator were in the early stages, and if anything jeopardised Quintus' ambitions for his daughter, he would be furious. When it was discovered, as it surely would be, that Horatia had spent an evening with Felix, and that Fortunata had helped set up the **Continued overleaf**

liaison with such a notorious man, she knew who would bear the brunt of the punishment. Not the spoiled daughter, that was for sure.

"Well, why are you waiting?" Horatia waved her hand irritably at Fortunata, "And hurry back. I need you to attend to my hair – Oh! Look at that! What were you thinking giving me soiled clothes to wear? You really must be more careful! Here," she said removing her tunic. "Take it to be cleaned today."

Fortunata would be punished when she got home. It was unavoidable. She couldn't possibly visit all the necessary shops in the forum, deliver Horatia's message and take the tunic to the fuller's, this side of noon, and that would mean trouble. But what choice did a slave have?

Fortunata held the basket of shopping firmly to her chest and dodged through the crowded street. She'd delivered the message to Felix's villa and now she only had to take the tunic to the fuller's.

Running lightly across the stepping stones in the road, she avoided the foul water that lay pooled in the gutters. The smell was bad enough but she knew it was about to worsen. Ahead were the buckets of urine that passers-by topped up when their need arose and she could hear the slaves singing in the fuller's, as they stamped up and down on the soiled clothes in a stone bath of urine.

As she entered the shop, the smell was almost overpowering and she gave silent thanks that she belonged to Quintus rather than Stephanus, the fuller.

"Fortunata? Fortunata! Is it really you?" A young man had stopped stamping in the bath and was waving.

"Antonius!" Fortunata's jaw dropped. She hadn't seen her childhood friend for many years. Since she'd become a slave, she hadn't encountered anyone from her city, so to unexpectedly come across Antonius, was a miracle.

"Get on with your work!" Stephanus lashed out at the slaves with a whip.

Fortunata lowered her gaze, not wanting to be the cause of a beating for her friend, although she longed to talk to him and to find out how he'd come to be working in the fuller's. He hadn't been there the last time she'd called.

Glancing up surreptitiously, she avoided eye contact as she watched him stamping on the clothes, and while Stephanus chatted with a customer, she couldn't help noticing that during the intervening years, the skinny boy she'd once known had become a man.

His legs were now finely muscled and his chest broad. In fact, if he hadn't called out to her, she probably wouldn't have recognised him at all.

Stephanus turned his attention to Fortunata and snatched the tunic from her. "Tell your mistress, I'll have this delivered tomorrow," he said ushering her out of the shop before she distracted his slave further.

Fortunata hesitated at the door. She wanted one last chance to look at Antonius, but she could feel Stephanus' eyes on her back and dared not turn.

To buy her a few more moments in the shop, she stepped to one side, allowing two other slaves to enter and hoped they would distract the owner while she at least gave Antonius a goodbye smile. How cruel to have found him after so long, yet be unable to speak to him.

She was so deep in thought that for a

second, she didn't notice the deep rumbling that came from beneath her feet.

Around her, people froze, their eyes looking left and right for the cause of the noise. In the street, the clip-clop of hooves and the clatter of wheels on the stone streets stopped, as everyone waited and listened.

Then the screaming began as the earth shuddered in a series of tremors, throwing people this way and that, breaking timbers and shaking roof tiles down on to the panic below. In the fuller's, slaves were thrown out of the bath and as Stephanus' money box crashed to the floor, he crawled about grabbing coins and thrusting them back in the wooden chest.

"Fortunata!" Antonius rushed towards her and helped her gently to her feet. "Are you hurt?"

"I…I don't think so. Are you?"

"No, I'm fine."

"You! On your knees with the others

Continued overleaf

Continued from previous page

and pick up my money!" Stephanus shouted at Antonius, grabbing him and forcing him to the floor, "I know exactly how much was there and if anything is missing there'll be trouble!" He kicked out viciously.

"Out!" he said to Fortunata. She picked up her basket and without daring to look back for Antonius, slipped out into the pandemonium on the street.

Her heart was still beating madly. There had been a few minor tremors over the previous few days but she'd never experienced anything like this. How could the whole city have moved like that? Were the gods angry?

Claudia, as if she'd discussed it with them and was satisfied that was an end to the matter. Then she turned her attention back to the artist, who worked nervously under her close scrutiny.

It was dark the next morning when Fortunata started sweeping the entrance hall. Everything had to be perfect for the feast that evening and the slaves were up earlier than usual.

At first, she didn't hear or recognise the sound that came from the street but as it grew louder and more insistent, she realised it was Antonius whistling a tune they'd both sung as children.

The other slaves were too busy to

"The gods are appeased," announced Claudia as if she'd discussed it with them

For once, luck was with her, if it could be considered lucky to have been knocked to the ground in an earthquake. Quintus' villa had suffered slight damage during the earth tremor and in the confusion, she'd crept into the villa, put the shopping in the kitchen and joined the other slaves who were cleaning up. Roof tiles were soon replaced and dust was swept up, but part of the fresco in the triclinium, where the feast would take place the following day, was cracked. Claudia was inconsolable and slaves were sent to search for an artist who could repair the wall at once.

There were several further shocks throughout the day but they were mild, half-hearted tremors that only lasted a second or so and did no further damage to the villa.

"The gods are appeased," announced

notice as she slipped out of the main door into the street. Antonius was standing in the shadows, holding a bundle of cleaned tunics and she flung her arms round his neck, holding him tightly.

"Fortunata, it's wonderful to see you! I've dreamed so often about the time we spent together! I didn't believe I'd ever see you again!" He lifted her off her feet.

Tears streamed down her cheeks as she clung to him.

"How did you know where to find me?"

"I volunteered to make the deliveries today," he said handing her Horatia's tunic. "I had to see you before I leave."

"Leave? Why? Where's Stephanus sending you?"

He shook his head, "He's not sending me anywhere. I'm going to escape."

"Are you mad?" she exclaimed.

"As soon as Stephanus leaves for the coast this evening, I'm going. By the time he discovers I'm missing, it'll be too late."

"But you'll be caught! Slaves are always caught! And then you'll be flogged… or branded… or killed!"

He shook his head.

"I think there's going to be enough of a diversion for me to get away. Do you remember my father's old slave, who taught us to fly kites?"

"Yes."

"Well, he came from the Far East and he told me about a mountain that trembled for several days and then spat fire and molten rock. A city was severely damaged."

"But that was just a story."

"No, it was true. All the earth tremors we've had over the last few days and the smoke coming from the mountain. They're signs. There's going to be some sort of disaster and by the time the city has recovered, I'll be gone."

"You're going to gamble your life on a disaster?" She looked at him in horror.

"It's now or never. Come with me!"

She shook her head sadly.

"I'd better go before we are seen."

"I'll come by before I leave and whistle our tune. I'll wait until midnight…"

After noon, a thick, grey cloud blotted out the sun and stones began to fall from the sky. Despite their size, they weighed very little and as they landed, they clattered and bounced on the pavements and roofs. Inside the villa, Claudia and Horatia were both hysterical, although for different reasons. There were not enough slaves to prepare the feast to Claudia's satisfaction and to sweep away the stones that were mounting up on the pavement outside the front door. When heavier rocks began to rain down, threatening to injure anyone not under shelter, she became frantic.

"No one will venture out in this!" she shouted at Quintus. "The evening's going to be a disaster! Let's leave for our country villa and organise another evening when this… whatever it is… stops," she said, waving her hand angrily at the sky.

"No! I have too much invested in this evening to cancel it now. We will carry on as planned."

Horatia, meanwhile, had received a message from Felix regretfully informing her he was leaving the city that night.

Fortunata had been the unlucky messenger who had received a beating for delivering the disappointing news. It wasn't the last thrashing she, or the other slaves, received during the afternoon which saw the ominous grey cloud thicken and darken, lit only by flashes of lightning.

It was while Fortunata was sweeping stones away from the front door that she heard Antonius whistling their tune. He was sheltering under an overhanging roof

Continued overleaf

Continued from previous page

opposite and she hurried across the road, her hands over her head for protection. She doubted anyone in the villa would notice her among the carts and crowds who stampeded through the streets.

"Come with me now, Fortunata! There's so much confusion, by the time anyone misses us, we'll be long gone."

"I… I…" Fortunata looked fearfully over her shoulder. Claudia's angry shouts could be heard even over the din of the frenzied street.

He grabbed her shoulders. "I'll look after you," he said, "with my life."

She winced as his thumbs pressed on the bruises Horatia and Claudia had inflicted earlier.

"You're hurt," he said, releasing her, "Fortunata, this is no life for us…"

"You're right," she said, suddenly determined. "Let's go now. Quickly – before I lose my nerve."

By the time they reached the city gate, the light stones had formed deep drifts and Antonius kept firm hold of her hand as they pushed through the confusion.

Choking ash now filled the air and Antonius tore a piece of cloth from his cloak for Fortunata to place over her mouth and nose. Most people were heading for the coast but Antonius found a farmer who was travelling east and begged him to give them a lift on his cart.

"You can hide among the jars and barrels. If anyone finds you, I'll deny I knew you were there. I don't want trouble with the authorities. But I was a slave once. I know what it's like to want yer freedom."

Antonius held Fortunata as they lay among the barrels, concealed under a covering of straw. He cushioned her with his body against the jolting of the cart and whispered memories from their childhood in her ear, trying to soothe her fears.

After several hours, he felt her body relax as she fell into an exhausted sleep and he cleared the straw from his face, so he could look up at the sky.

It was dark – not because of that smothering grey cloud, but because of the moonless night. The air was fresh and clean and he breathed deeply.

Finally, the cart stopped and the farmer helped them down.

"This is as far as I'm going but if I were you, I'd go back. Throw yerselves on yer master's mercy. Tell 'im you panicked. Those city people are rich an' powerful, an' as soon as they've cleaned up the mess, they'll be after any escaped slaves.

"After them bad earthquakes nearly twenty years ago they soon patched the city up and it was business as usual. It'll take more than a bit of stone and ash dropping from the sky to bring Pompeii to its knees. It'll be up and runnin' in no time. You mark my words"

"Thanks, but we'll head east and take our chances," said Antonius reaching for Fortunata's hand and leading her away.

Ahead, the sun peeped over the mountains promising a fine, clear day.

• •

THE AUTHOR SAYS...

"Recently, I was inspired when my husband and I visited the ruins of Pompeii and Heraculaneum and were amazed at how intact many of the buildings were, and our guide painted a vivid picture of life immediately before the eruption of Vesuvius."

Brain BOOSTERS

Missing Link

The answer to each clue is a word which has a link with each of the three words listed. This word may come at the end (eg **HEAD** linked with **BEACH, BIG, HAMMER**), at the beginning (eg **BLACK** linked with **BEAUTY, BOARD and JACK**) or a mixture of the two (eg **STONE** linked with **HAIL, LIME and WALL**).

ACROSS

1 Awakening, Health, Joke (4)
3 Pox, Run, Spring (7)
9 Barrel, Chocolate, Dog (7)
10 House, Singer, Soap (5)
11 Bitter, Grass, Sole (5)
13 Drill, Grip, Oliver (5)
14 Car, Notes, Sparingly (4)
16 Club, Culture, Hostel (5)
18 Bridle, Cycle, War (4)
19 Home, Land, Ship (5)
21 Bowling, Finch, Grocer (5)
23 Blue, Bone, Killer (5)
24 Parrot, Statement, Victim (7)
25 Birthday, Christmas, Tense (7)
26 Coal, Grill, Lady (4)

DOWN

1 Brer, Hutch, Jack (6)
2 Attorney, Lake, Nurse (8)
4 Stand, Top, Trick (3)
5 Court, Derby, Prince (5)
6 Break, Handed, Song (4)
7 Conscience, Party, Verdict (6)
8 Bare, Poker, Two (5)
12 Field, Harvest, Hole (5)
15 Board, Club, Victoria (8)
17 Living, Opinion, Truth (6)
18 Cocktail, Cracker, King (5)
20 Bean, Front, Marathon (6)
21 Lucky, Wild, Work (5)
22 Band, Camel, Cut (4)
24 Belt, Club, Oven (3)

Hidden word in the shaded squares: _____

Time To Face The Fireworks

Clare has never explained to her daughter why Bonfire Night is such a big deal. Now it's the other way round

By A. Millward

I t's at moments like these that I wish they gave out handbooks for parenting.

I mean, it's ridiculous. I've been standing here on my landing for the last five minutes, clutching a mug of hot chocolate, having a stare-down with my daughter's bedroom door.

The very door that was slammed shut a few hours ago after I told Becca there was no chance she was going out tonight. The house has only just stopped reverberating.

I'd been hanging some clothes in the airing cupboard when I'd overheard her making plans to meet someone. Then I'd heard her mention "fireworks"…

"But, Mum, I have to go."

Facing off in her room, I'd felt outnumbered. Becca had positioned herself in front of her shrine-like wall dedicated to animals. Posters, shelves groaning with ornaments and cuddly toys, and more recently pictures of her favourite residents at the sanctuary she's been volunteering at. All these eyes looked out at me pleadingly. It had felt like a thousand against one.

"And why's that?"

"Because…" But before she could finish, her violet-glossed lips clamped shut. "People are expecting me, that's all."

I felt for her then. My little girl who's no longer my little girl. Blazing blue eyes all the more intense for the Cleopatra-like eyeliner and, as usual, dressed in fifty shades of black.

"Well, you shouldn't make promises you can't keep. I'm sorry, Becca, but this time no means no."

I'd beat a hasty retreat before any more questions came. But just before the prodigious door slam, she'd called out: "It's not always about us, you know, Mum."

So here I am, hovering with my peace offering getting cold and mulling over her parting shot. Around me, the normally pale walls are playing chameleon, imitating the blasts of colour beyond the window which have been playing on my nerves all night.

Get a grip, Clare. She's thirteen now, not three. You can't keep her under lock and key for ever. Do you honestly think a hot chocolate is going to make this all go away, even if it is swimming with mini marshmallows and whipped cream?

In lieu of no better ideas, I tap on the door. "Becca, love, I made some cocoa."

Continued overleaf

Another knock. "Honey? Look, I know you're mad at me, but I have my reasons. Perhaps we could talk about it."

Silence. Well, the closest you get to silence on Bonfire Night anyway.

"Well, look, I'm going to put this cocoa down out here…" As I bend, my shoulder bumps the door, enough to nudge it ajar. When there's no immediate scream of protest, an icy dread creeps over me.

"Becca?"

Before I even enter her room, I know she's not here.

Thankfully my mother's at home. "Mum? You've got to help me. Becca's run away. I know where she is – I think – but I could really do with an extra pair of eyes."

"Clare, you're going to have to slow down. You sound like you've got yourself in a terrible state… wait, are you driving?"

"Yes, it's hands-free, though. I'm fine."

"You sound about as far from fine as it's possible to be. Where is she?"

"I can't be a hundred percent. I wish I could, but this is all I have. She was talking about fireworks, Mum. I heard her say it more than once. I told her she couldn't go, but she went anyway. Mum, if anything…"

I can't finish my sentence. I can only imagine all the thoughts swirling round my mother's head – all the things I'd probably have said if I were in her position… Which is why I've never loved her more than when she replies, "OK. I'll meet you there."

This time of year always puts me on edge. Bonfire Night. Though, of course, the way it goes on these days, it's more like Bonfire Fortnight. Then there's all the other fireworks being let off left, right and centre, year-round, for weddings, birthdays, Fridays – pretty much any celebration, it seems.

I had a bad experience when I was just a little older than Becca, which has cast a long shadow over my life.

It all began on an evening eerily similar to this. An argument with my parents

Johnny's mate had a box of fireworks and was letting them off intermittently

"All I heard her talking about was a park and meeting someone by a fountain. And I'm pretty sure she mentioned the 45 bus stopping there. Or it may have been 25. Anyway, I checked out bus routes and I'm heading to that huge park over town, near the Redhill estate. Do you know it?"

"Yes, I think so. But what makes you so sure that's where she'll be? Besides, don't you think Becca's old enough to go with her friends to the park?"

about going out with friends on fireworks night. I'd been in bed with the flu for almost a week and Mum told me, in no uncertain terms, that if I wasn't well enough to go to school, there was no way I was going out on a bitter November night.

"And certainly not wearing that," Dad had helpfully added from behind his newspaper.

But my mind was made up. Johnny Swithuns was going to be there. And I'd heard rumours he'd been asking if I was going to be there. As far as I was concerned, when opportunities like that came along, you didn't let them pass.

So, just like Becca, I had sneaked out. Of course, I needed some moral support, so after a lot of persuading I'd managed to drag out Anita, despite the fact she hated the cold and wasn't fussed about fireworks. But what else are best friends for, if not being there in your hour of need?

It was just a small bit of wasteland, a ring of tree stumps and crates around a rather sorry-looking bonfire. One of Johnny's mates had "borrowed" a box of fireworks from his dad's newsagents and was letting them off intermittently but nobody was particularly paying attention. There were a few cans being passed around and Johnny was strumming his guitar.

And that's when I uttered those fateful words. "Swap with me, Anita."

I had intentionally chosen a seat directly opposite Johnny so I could see him – and he could see me – but the growing flames of the fire were getting in the way.

Having had a little cider, my friend was beginning to enjoy herself. She'd smiled at me knowingly as she got to her feet.

"Of course. Can't have the view being disrupted, can we?"

I was only vaguely aware of the shouting a few minutes later. I was still a bit spaced-out from the flu, and what attention I did have was fixated on Johnny's fingers as they plucked at the guitar strings, the dancing of the flames in his dark eyes…

But then the urgency of the shouts took on another level.

"Everybody, out the way!"

The next thing I knew, I could feel scratchy grass against my cheek and a body half-sprawled over me.

"Are you all right, Clare?"

I didn't have to open my eyes to know it was Johnny's voice. He must have virtually leapt over the fire to push me out of the way. Of what? I was half-tempted not to reply. Perhaps he'd give me the kiss of life? But curiosity got the better of me. "I think so."

Sheepishly Johnny clambered off so that I could sit up.

"What happened?"

"One of the rockets fell over. It shot right at us."

Others were also getting to their feet. There was lots of nervous giggling. Lairy cheers by the boys. Someone was laying into the guy who set up the AWOL firework.

Then through it all came the scream. My scream, I later realised. Because one
Continued overleaf

Continued from previous page

person wasn't laughing off the near-miss. One person wasn't getting up.

It was Anita.

Pulling up by the fountain I'm praying is the one Becca had mentioned, I jump as a thunder-like boom lights up the sky. This will be the nearest I have been to fireworks since that night…

Normally that fear would paralyse me, as the memory of Anita flashes inside my head. Not just my best friend lying there, so still on the ground. But the days, weeks, months that followed.

In many ways, she was so lucky. Her hearing mostly recovered, the burns healed. After a few months, you'd never have guessed what she'd been through. At least on the outside.

I haven't ever been able to comprehend the extent of the inner, psychological scars. Not that she ever blamed me – for dragging her there, for swapping places. Not any of it. Somehow that made it worse.

My guilt only grew as I found excuses to let our friendship peter out, like an untended fire. *It should have been me* was all I could think when I was around her. *It should have been me.* These days, the odd Facebook status or Like is the closest we get to contact.

But tonight I'm not here for me, I'm here for Becca. At least, that is if this is even the right place… There must be dozens of parks with fountains having firework displays tonight. It's a relief to see a familiar figure hurrying towards me.

"Sorry for getting you out like this," I begin to say. "You had every right to refuse, considering the circumstances…"

"Shh, don't be silly," she says, hugging me into silence – knowing it's exactly what I need. "Now, I'd ask what our Becca is wearing, but I have a feeling I know what the answer will be. On the plus side, there probably aren't many people here wearing only black."

"True," I say. "Though on the down side, it is night time."

We split up to cover more ground. As I move through the clusters of people, my suspicions that this is no official display go from doubt to certainty. It's mainly teenagers here and everyone seems to be drinking. There are no barriers and no security officers and I can see shadowy figures running across the fields, lighting fireworks by hand then dashing away. It's as if history's repeating itself…

the Bonfire Night bubble for ever. I just wasn't prepared for it to burst tonight.

"Any joy?" Mum asks, as we reconvene on the other side of the park, at the border of the shadowy woodland.

I shake my head, unable to stop contemplating the worst.

Mum squeezes my arm. "She'll be fine. Just hanging out with her mates moaning about her over-protective mother."

I allow myself a smile. "And the rest."

"Right, let's do another sweep. Meet back on the other side in fifteen."

As I head back towards the crowd and the deafening booms and screeches above, my nerves already shot, I don't think I could have done this without my calm, ever-rational mother. Of course, she's right about Becca. She'll be fine.

My phone buzzes. "I've found her. She's fine – but you'd best come quick"

Come on, Becca, where are you?

It had been so easy when she was younger. Countless ways of keeping a safe distance between my daughter and the November threat. Lots of well-timed holidays. A new game or movie – "Let's close the curtains and get cosy".

Then, when she was a bit older: "Watching them from behind the window is so much better anyway. It's freezing out there." Or "Fireworks look better from behind glass, it's been proven." (OK, so I had to cross my fingers for that last one.)

But even adults know the best fireworks are on TV, right? They spare no expense for that London display and you get all those panoramic shots.

I'd always known I couldn't maintain

Sulky and frustrated, but fine. Perhaps it's even best we don't find her – if we do, she probably won't speak to me for weeks for embarrassing her in front of her mates. Who knows, perhaps she has a Johnny Swithuns of her own?

I've almost convinced myself this is all a ridiculous over-reaction, when my phone starts buzzing.

"I've found her," Mum says without any introductions. "She's fine, but you'd best come quick."

Mum is hovering nervously at the edge of the crowd and she points me in the right direction. Jostling my way through, suddenly there she is. My Becca.
Continued overleaf

Continued from previous page
Sitting on the grass. The only person looking away from the fireworks. Part of me can't believe it was this easy.

"Becca?"

She looks up but it's as if she doesn't see me – like I'm a ghost. As a white firework goes off ahead, I see the mascara tear tracks across her cheeks.

"Hey, what's the matter?" I kneel down beside her. Her hands are freezing and I rub them between mine to warm up.

"Oh, Mum. I should never have come. It's all been one huge, epic failure."

"How do you mean?"

She looks away, still fighting, still holding back.

hands me one from a bundle of flyers.

There's a photo montage of dogs, cats and other animals. Then printed below in big letters:

THE NIGHTMARE BEFORE
CHRISTMAS
DON'T LET ANIMALS SUFFER ON
BONFIRE NIGHT!
BAN FIREWORKS

"You were staging a protest?"

She scoffs. "Well, the worst protest ever in the history of protests. Only seven people turned up. Over a hundred signed up to the Facebook group. Even the ones that came got cold, hungry and bored

"Oh, Mum. I should never have come here. It's all been one huge, epic failure..."

"Look, Becca…" I begin, before leaping out of my skin as a squealing firework seems to whizz right over us.

"Mum, they're just bundles of carbon with chemicals to give them different colours. We know what they are – we don't need to fear them." Her hands now squeeze mine, roles reversed.

I manage a wobbly smile.

"I wish I had your confidence."

"But imagine it from a dog's point of view. Or a horse's. Or a cat's. Any animal, really. Now they do have something to be scared of. They have no idea what is happening. Just huge explosions that must sound like the world ending. That's why I'm here."

"What do you mean?"

Without hesitation now, she opens her mini-rucksack – in black, of course – and

within an hour and went home."

"But you stayed."

"Well, someone had to. The sanctuary is only a few roads from here – they'll hear all of this. Not to mention all the pets living around this estate.

"And did you know a deer park opened in that woodland last month? They must be petrified. When I heard some kids at school were organising this big fireworks party here, I knew I had to do something. Fat lot of difference I've made."

"You could always have called the authorities…"

"I'm a protester, Mum, not a snitch."

I think for a moment. I vaguely remember seeing a phone box, close to the entrance of the park.

"Then how does an anonymous tip-off from a concerned local sound?"

An inner brightness enters her eyes, nothing to do with the fireworks.

"You'd do that?"

I wrap an arm round my beautiful warrior daughter, because even warriors need hugs sometimes. "A very wise soul once told me that sometimes we have to do things because others can't."

Her cheeks redden.

"Well, now seems as good a time as any for me to start. Come on, let's go home."

I'm sorry. For sneaking out." We've been driving for about fifteen minutes when Becca breaks the silence. "I didn't want to disobey you, I promise I didn't. But all the animals that live over there, they have no one to fight their battles."

"You could have said why you wanted to go…" I say quietly.

"And you would have let me? Be real, Mum. Even if a protest wasn't enough to have you barring the door, I was still coming to a fireworks display. Just what is it with you and fireworks anyway?"

It's the question I've been dodging for years. But this time, there's no avoiding it. Just the way it had been for my poor friend all that time ago.

"There's something I need to tell you. But let's get home first, hey? I'll put on some cocoa so we can warm up."

I can feel her eyeing me for a moment, perhaps wondering if I'm going to stick to my word, but then her inner child takes over.

"Can we have mini-marshmallows and whipped cream?"

"Of course we can, love." The rest of the journey home, I have to fight hard to suppress a grin. Because perhaps I'm doing half-OK as a mum without that parenting handbook after all.

As for the Good Friend handbook, that's a whole other matter, I think as we pull into the drive.

"Mum? Are you coming?"

"Give me a sec, love. I just need to send a quick email. Get the kettle on. I'll be right in."

By the time Becca has disappeared inside, I have pulled up Anita on Facebook and opened a blank new message.

Like they always do at this point, my fingers seize up. But fear and guilt have been my tethering me to the past for far too long. Tonight my amazing daughter has shown me many things, not least that I have more inner strength than I ever knew.

Fireworks continue to shake the night, but I refuse to let them bother me. *Let them roar. Let them dazzle. But don't let them rule your life any more, Clare.*

Dear Anita, I begin the message that's been years coming. *It's been far too long. But I hope you'll give me a chance to put that right. Let's meet soon. There's so much we need to talk about…*

When To See A Squirrel

Unless it was pixellated and had a points score attached, I doubted my grandson ever would…

By Pat Holness

I'm sipping camomile tea and catching up on the day's newspaper when a whirlwind in the form of Danny arrives.

My darling grandson has spiky gelled hair, blue eyes full of mischief and he functions in one mode only: full speed.

"Hi Gran!" Apparently it's not cool at the great age of eight to hug your grandmother, so he stands for a moment or two regarding me quizzically before venturing, "Have you made any brownies? Mum's told me you make brilliant ones!"

It's the first time Danny has ever been to stay with me on his own. He lives with his mum in Spain, and while she's here on business I am to have Danny all to myself.

Relieved to learn that chocolate cake is cool, I offer him one I made earlier.

"Awesome!"

Danny and I get this far before my daughter appears from the car where she's been unpacking, weighed down by bags.

"I don't think we've forgotten anything." Kate pushes her hair out of her eyes and comes over to give me a kiss. "I'll put his things in the spare room. It's brilliant of you to have Danny to stay," she adds. "He's been excited about the visit

for ages. Oh – and he's come well equipped with games and stuff, so you needn't worry about him. He'll amuse himself. Kids these days love all the technical gadgetry, don't they?"

My heart sinks. What I know about computers and the like could be written on the back of a postage stamp.

Once Kate has gone, Danny removes his belongings from the case and is instantly welded to a small piece of technology with a brightly coloured screen and an aggravating bleep.

"What would you like to do once you've settled in?" I try tentatively. "I don't think I'm into tablets – other than the one I'm about to take to cure the headache your noisy game's giving me."

I didn't mention that I'd planned a walk in the woods and a picnic in the park.

"Dunno." Danny is lost in his own world.

The next half hour passes with his eyes riveted to the game and his fingers dancing across the screen.

"Can you show me how to play?" I venture at last, remembering the old saying, *If you can't beat them…*

This gets Danny's attention. His blue eyes widen in wonder.

"Sure," he says.

It takes a while. In fact it takes quite a

long while, but eventually I am up and running with the game. Reluctantly I have to admit it's exercising my brain. It's also addictive. Danny shows me more of the attractions on his tablet and I am overawed at the wonder of it.

"Mum does her shopping online," Danny tells me and with a swift click he shows me something he calls an app.

Totally fascinated by this new world, I'm like a mature Alice in Wonderland falling down the rabbit-hole.

Next day I'm ready for more.

Once breakfast is cleared away, Danny disappears to his room, appearing a few minutes later clad in anorak and walking boots. He even has a red bobble hat.

"Aren't you going to show me a bit more stuff on your tablet?" I ask, trying not to sound too pleading.

"Not right now, Gran. I think we ought to go outdoors today. It's good for us."

I can't believe this is happening. Here's my thoroughly modern grandson Danny all togged up for the great outdoors and bossing me about like he's my grandad.

"We can play on the tablet when we get back, but Mum said you've got some fabulous woods round here. There might even be squirrels. I've never been close to a real live squirrel. Can we go now?"

I look out of the window. It's a dull day. The clouds look like rain. What I'd really like to do is play games on Danny's tablet.

Instead, I reach for my coat.

"Come on, then," I say.

● ●

THE AUTHOR SAYS...

"I wrote this story after noticing how my grandchildren cope wonderfully with technology one minute and with playing outdoors the next!"

Stories At Bedtime

A parental split is always unsettling for a child, but it seemed Alice had her own way of coping

By Amanda Brittany

D o you know, Grandma, that the lady across the road is a witch?" Alice looked up at me with wide blue eyes, her mass of fair hair surrounding her pale face.

"Is she indeed?" I said, as I washed up a saucepan, smiling as my six-year-old granddaughter began dashing around the kitchen pretending to ride a broom.

She stopped and nodded excitedly. She'd always had an imagination that J. K. Rowling might be envious of, but since her dad left six months ago, I wondered whether she was disappearing a little too far into her fantasy world.

I dried my hands on the tea towel and crouched so we were eye to eye. I pushed a wayward curl from her forehead and said gently, "I'm sure the lady across the road isn't really a witch."

"But she is, Grandma. She really, really, really is." She paused for a moment, dropping her eyes to the floor. "But she's not a bad witch with scary long nails."

She raised her little hands, and dragged her fingers through the air as though they were ferocious claws. "Grrrr," she said, pulling a funny face.

"You sound more like a tiger, Alice," I said with a laugh.

"Well, do you know, Grandma, that Mr Brown next door has got one of those?"

"A tiger? Has he indeed?"

She gave three little nods, her hair swinging. "And my teacher has got panthers in her kitchen."

"Black panthers, aye?"

"Don't be silly, Gran," she said, screwing up her face. "Pink panthers. She walks them in the middle of the night on sparkly leads when everyone is sleeping."

"Really?"

She nodded again.

"Well I think," I declared, rising, "that we need to get you bathed and into your pyjamas. And then maybe we could watch *Frozen* again?"

"Yay!" she cheered, trotting obediently from the kitchen.

As I finished clearing away I thought of Alice picking at her fish fingers earlier. "Do you know, Grandma," she'd said, "that fish haven't really got fingers?"

It was the first time I'd heard her say something real for a long time, but she hadn't smiled. It was as though her imagination was helping her through.

Continued overleaf

Continued from previous page

Alice's dad, Elliot, and my daughter, Jenny, got married ten years ago. But when Alice came along, it seemed to put pressure on them both.

Neither could afford to give up their jobs, and they seemed, over the years, to lose that special something that had held them together. They drifted apart and eventually Elliot left, both agreeing they needed space.

I had hoped they would see sense. Eventually see they were made for each other. But now Jenny was going out every Friday with the girls while I babysat Alice.

I felt incredibly sad that she couldn't see she was meant to be with Elliot.

Later that evening, I snuggled on the sofa, Alice in her Hello Kitty pyjamas.

"Do you know, Grandma," she said as she leaned her head against me, "that the lady in the bank is an opera?'

"An opera?"

"Like Shrek."

"Oh, an ogre?"

"Yes. And that's the very, very truth, because Mummy says so."

"Really?"

"Yes, And do you know, Grandma, that Daddy is really a handsome knight who is going to come on his big white horse and take Mummy in his arms, and we'll all live happily ever after?"

Tears stung my eyes.

"Well that would be nice, Alice," I said. "But if it doesn't happen, you must remember that they will both love you forever."

"But it will happen, Grandma," she said, and I hugged her tighter.

After the Disney film, I tucked Alice in her bed, read her story and kissed her forehead. "Goodnight, sweetheart," I said, pulling the door half closed.

Later, once I was back downstairs, I heard Jenny's key in the door. She appeared in the lounge, glowing – just as she had the week before, and the week before that.

"Hello, Mum," she said. And then I saw him behind her.

"Elliot," I said, as he put his arm round Jenny. "What are you doing here?"

"We're going to give it another go," Jenny said, smiling. "We've been seeing each other for a few weeks, but we didn't want to say anything until we were absolutely sure."

I jumped up and hugged them both.

"Daddy?" It was a bleary-eyed Alice, standing behind them.

Elliot scooped her into his arms, and she hugged his neck as though she'd never let go.

"Do you know, Grandma?" she said, looking at me. "I thought I heard the sound of hooves coming down the road."

• •

THE AUTHOR SAYS...

"The inspiration for this story came from when my son was little. He would always say 'Do you know, Mummy?' and then come up with the most imaginative stories."

Brain BOOSTERS

Sudoku 1   Sudoku 2

Fill in each of the blank squares with the numbers 1 to 9, so that each row, each column and each 3x3 cell contains all the numbers from 1 to 9.

Sudoku 1

			4					
9		6	8					
		1	7	2		6		4
			2			8		
	8	2	5		3	9	7	
		5			4			
3		9		5	1	4		
				8	1		3	
			3					

Sudoku 2

3	7					2		
				7		4		
					3			8
	8						5	
1						3		
6		5	8				7	
	9		4					
8		1			9			6
	6		3	5				4

Word Wheel

You have ten minutes to find as many words as possible using the letters in the wheel. Each word must be three letters or more and contain the central letter. Use each letter once and no plurals, foreign words or proper nouns are allowed. There is at least one nine-letter word.

Average: 35 words
Good: 36-52 words
Excellent: 53-69 words

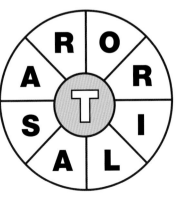

Step by Step

The agile boys in the park seemed a world away from my injured, dispirited husband...

By Mhairi Grant

T he cup of tea from the van warmed my hands as I watched the boys skateboarding.

They wore those low-slung, loose-fitting jeans and cargo shorts and attacked the slope with grace and confidence. The wheels of their skateboards sparked the concrete and then with a flick of a foot, the skateboard was in their hand, ready for the next challenge. The more daring did jumps and spins.

They did not feel the cold. But I did. I should go home, but I wasn't ready. I needed time out. It was hard work always trying to be positive, to keep up another person's spirit twenty-four-seven.

I sipped the tea from its plastic cup. The heat was momentary, leaving me colder than ever. I drained it, scrunched the cup up and binned it.

I needed to keep moving. I walked through the park and thought of Scott. He had fallen off some scaffolding at work and had seriously damaged his spine.

"I'll be walking in no time," he'd said – in the beginning.

But somewhere between the physiotherapy sessions and visits to the consultant he'd lost heart. My rugby-playing husband, who had climbed most of the Munros, had given up.

As I retraced my steps I realised that the park had emptied. The skateboarders had gone – all but for one boy.

He stood with the skateboard by his side, looking at the slope. It was hardly a Munro but I sensed that to the boy it could have been Everest.

I slowed my steps as he went for the gentler slope. He fell, gut-wrenchingly hard. But he got up and tried again.

I stopped to watch, aware that he hadn't seen me.

T he sun was beginning to set as I stepped back into the trees to watch. The boy tried again and again, sometimes not falling but stepping off.

"Go for it," I murmured, at one stage, as the boy hovered, bruised and uncertain.

He did. Finally he managed to get from one side to the other without falling off. I felt like clapping, but sensed that his humiliation would be complete if he knew that someone had witnessed his attempts.

"I wish you could see this boy, Scott," I whispered.

Continued overleaf

Continued from previous page

It was at that moment I realised my deep-buried anger at Scott for giving up. And for the long-term implications it had for me – my husband in a wheelchair.

Selfish, I knew – but up to the accident I had been used to leaning on Scott. He had been my rock.

I broke cover from the trees and walked away. I had not gone far when I heard the shout.

"Yes!"

I smiled as I imagined the skateboarder punching the air in delight at yet another slope conquered. If only life was so simple.

The sky was awash with red as I turned into our street. A figure was sitting on our garden wall. My heart thudded unnaturally

Like the skateboarder, Scott had his pride. He tried his crutches when no one was there

loudly as I stared. It was Scott. And there was no wheelchair in sight.

"Hi Zoe," he said, as I stared at the crutches. "You've been gone so long, I started to worry. You didn't have your phone with you."

"Sorry," I murmured. "I just went for a walk. Do you want a cup of tea?"

"I would love a cup."

I walked past him into the house. Like the skateboarder, Scott had his pride. He tried the crutches when there was no one to witness his humiliation. I brushed away my tears as I put on the kettle.

"Tea!" I shouted, a little while later.

I won't go out and help him, I thought. *I won't. I won't fuss or smother him like I have been doing – hovering over him every moment of his waking life and*

haranguing medical staff for answers. I have to learn to stand back.

It was painful to watch. I busied myself while surreptitiously looking out of the window at the sweat on his forehead, his shaking limbs, his tortured, infinitesimally slow steps. Still, Scott was walking… he was walking! My heart sang.

Yes, I was selfish. I wanted my old husband back. Meanwhile I would be his rock — but only when he wanted me to be.

THE AUTHOR SAYS…

"It's only natural to fuss when a loved one has been hurt or injured. But there are times when one has to stand back and let them take things at their own pace."

Party Waffle Bites

Use a waffle iron or pan to make these – or simply use the batter to make drop scones instead.

Preparation time: 15 minutes
Cooking time: 12 minutes

Ingredients (Makes 4-6)
+ **125g plain flour**
+ **½tsp bicarbonate of soda**
+ **½tsp salt**
+ **230ml buttermilk**
+ **1 egg**
+ **A few drops of vegetable oil**
+ **80g medium fat soft cheese**
+ **80g mature Cheddar, finely grated**
+ **1 fig, sliced into 8**
+ **100g red pepper houmous**
+ **A few cucumber slices**
+ **30g roasted peppers, from a jar**
+ **Herb sprigs, to garnish**

1 Sift the flour, bicarbonate of soda and salt into a large bowl. Add the buttermilk and egg and beat with a whisk to make a smooth batter. Leave to stand for 20min.

2 Brush a waffle pan or waffle iron with vegetable oil. Add about 2tbsp batter to each waffle section and cook for 1-2min until the underneath is golden brown. Turn over to cook the other side. Repeat to make 4 waffles. Cool.

3 Cut each waffle into 4. Mix the soft cheese and Cheddar together and use to top half the waffle pieces, placing a piece of fig on top.

4 Top the rest of the waffles with houmous, cucumber slices and strips of roasted red pepper. Garnish with herb sprigs, then serve.

Cook's tip: Use your imagination with the toppings, making the most of what you have available.

RECIPE AND FOOD STYLING: SUE ASHWORTH · PHOTOGRAPHY: JONATHAN SHORT

Five Sleeps 'Til Christmas

And all through the house there was chaos, piles of jobs still to do, and an overexcited Harry...

By **Camilla Kelly**

Five Sleeps to Go

Harry," I said, looking suspiciously at the advent calendar on his bedside table as I tucked him in, "what's today?"

"The twentieth."

"So how come doors twenty-one and twenty-two are open?"

He shrugged. "It came like that."

I should have known better than to let him have it in his room.

"And the chocolates were already gone?"

He nodded. "You should complain."

I looked at him, hard. No wonder he hadn't eaten my trial onion stuffing at dinner. He started to giggle.

I tickled him in the ribs and escalated the giggle into a roar of laughter.

"Are you going to stay in bed tonight?"

"Yes." He looked angelic.

"Promise? Because Father Christmas is on the lookout for naughty boys, you know."

"But Mum," he said, kissing my cheek, "I'm so good."

Four Sleeps to Go

And still no presents wrapped. "You promised to stay in bed last night," I reminded Harry as I pulled the duvet up to his chin with a gesture not unlike putting him in the stocks. "And five minutes later I caught you in the lounge."

"I was just looking at the lights."

If I couldn't trust him to stay in bed, I'd never have the chance to get his presents out from their hiding place. Even now he wriggled about to loosen his bedclothes, too excited to settle.

"How many sleeps is it till Christmas now, Mum?"

"Just four." I gave a shiver of panic.

"Four? That's ages!"

"Harry, why is there a puddle?"

He sat up. "Aw, has it melted? I left the window open and everything."

"You had a snowman inside, didn't you?"

"Just a little one."

I looked at the drenched wallpaper under the window as I pulled it shut.

"I like your optimism, little man, but keep them outdoors from now on, OK?"

"Sorry, Mum."

"And stay in bed, right?"

He saluted. He should have been exhausted after the evening we spent delivering cards, though mainly he'd been having a snowball fight with his dad as we went from house to house. I certainly was. But you could never trust a six-year-old to stay where you put him.

Continued overleaf

Three Sleeps to Go

Harry, stop jumping on the bed, it's time to get in now."

I could kill our neighbour for giving him an e-number-packed candy cane.

"Three to go, three to go, three to go!" he sang to the tune of *Let It Snow*.

He'd learned the song at the Christmas sing-along in the church hall, which we'd arrived to late after baking the reindeer cookies we were meant to bring. I'd been too busy thinking about all the work left to do to concentrate on the music, so it was nice to get another rendition of it.

I let him get to the end of the chorus but when he went back to the beginning I caught him around the middle and plopped him into bed.

"Bedtime, Harry."

"Are you going to wrap my presents?"

"You're not getting any presents. We sent them to a poor family in Africa."

"Did you?" he asked seriously. He didn't seem to mind the idea.

"Well, maybe we'll get you a couple more," I said fondly. "If you're good."

"I didn't touch the wrapping paper," he said suddenly, and quickly turned on his side and closed his eyes.

"Why do you say that?" I said.

"Just saying. Night, Mum."

On my way out I saw the mountain of ripped, Sellotape-encrusted wrapping paper in his bin. The whole roll's worth.

I deflated. Another job for tomorrow: buy new paper; wrap the presents I should have been wrapping this evening. On top of seeing if I could get a turkey from the butcher since I'd forgotten to order one…

From the hallway I heard the distinct sound of Harry jumping on his bed.

Two Sleeps to Go

Harry! What are you doing in there?"
He peered up at me from the bottom of my wardrobe where he sat crushing my shoe boxes. I cringed to think of my best shoes in there. Not to mention the ones under Rick, his chubbier cousin, who was beside Harry, shamefaced.

"Nothing," Harry said innocently.

"Don't tell fibs," his dad said, sternly. We'd been making up beds for my sister's family and I'd been about to ask him to pick up a turkey from the supermarket in the morning when he collected the online order, when we heard the thump from the wardrobe. "You were looking for presents, weren't you?"

I sighed. "You're even dragging your poor cousin into it. He's only been here five minutes! Come on, out of there."

They slumped out.

"And you didn't find anything, did you?" Jason said. "We keep telling you, naughty boys don't get presents."

Rick looked aghast.

"I'm really sorry, Uncle Jason!"

I shook my head.

"Harry, what am I going to do with you?"

One Sleep to Go

The veggies to prepare, the stockings to fill, and I still hadn't wrapped Harry's presents.

I didn't know where Jason was, and my sister had passed out in front of the TV. At least the kids were staying in bed.

I set the timer on the oven for the turkey and then remembered – we didn't have one.

I'd have to go to the supermarket. Hopefully it would be quiet this late in the evening, and hopefully they'd have a turkey left that wasn't too sad-looking.

I sank wearily into a chair, dreading the thought. All these weeks of preparing for Christmas and it still snuck up on you before you were ready.

I rang Jason to find out where he was.

"Sorry, love, I thought I'd be back by now. I'm in an endless queue to pay for your mum's gin and your dad's Scotch."

I slapped my forehead. Something else I'd forgotten. And worse…

"Jason, I can't believe it, I haven't got you anything!"

My whole body flushed with shame.

He chuckled. "That's all right."

"No, it's not! I found this place online that sells vintage record players… I meant to go today and pick it up but I didn't have the time."

"I can wait," he said mildly. "I know how hard you've been working."

"I feel terrible."

"Don't be daft. That's not what Christmas is about, is it?"

I hung up, knowing he was right, and yet it was really hard to hold on to that sentiment when there was always so much to do. But the warm appreciation I felt for Jason made me take a long moment of peace, and smile.

"Mum?"

Harry was at the door.

"What is it, Harry?"

"I need to tell you. I've been naughty."

"No! Really?"

He'd noticed there weren't any presents under the tree. Was he starting to panic? To his credit he looked sheepish.

"Yes. Dad gave me money to buy you a present but I spent it on Lego."

"I see."

"So I made you this instead."

He gave me a parcel so inexpertly wrapped that the paper was falling off. Inside was a snow globe made of a jam jar. In the glittery snow, smiling photos of Harry, Jason and I were propped around a plastic snowman. My heart melted.

"Thank you, Harry. It's perfect. Come on, back to bed."

"I don't want to miss Santa going past."

He pushed himself onto the windowsill and pulled the curtain around him.

I looked at the pile of washing up, and the sprouts waiting to be scored. I should send Harry to bed and get on with it.

But I was sick of being good. I was missing all the fun. At least Harry was enjoying himself.

I made a decision.

"How about we don't have a turkey tomorrow, Harry? How about cheese toasties instead?"

"Cheese toasties!" A roar of approval behind the curtain.

We could have turkey another day. For New Year, even. Seven days until then.

"Any room under there for me, Harry?"

We huddled together under the curtain. The sky was so clear you could see stars. In the valley, Christmas lights twinkled. For the first time I felt properly festive.

"Look!" He pointed to the blinking lights of an aeroplane. "Is that him?"

"Probably," I said, smiling. "He must be on his way here."

• •

THE AUTHOR SAYS…

"I never seem to have enough time at Christmas to do everything. I realised that I must be getting old when I started wishing Christmas wouldn't arrive so quickly!"

Santa Comes Knocking

Christmas was looking bleak for little Darren and his mum – until their neighbour lent a hand

By Ginny Swart

Weighed down with shopping bags, Anna Martens plodded up the cold cement staircase to the third floor in Jubilee Mansions.

Sometimes she wondered which Jubilee this dismal block was named for – certainly not the one celebrating the present Queen's fiftieth year on the throne.

The walls of the stairwell badly needed a coat of paint and the graffiti, which Anna washed off as often as she could, reappeared within a day or two. Loud voices from daytime TV shows followed her up the stairs from the second floor, and she thought longingly of her peaceful, neat little flat, her oasis just one flight further up.

Three small boys sat on the top step blocking her path. One she recognised as five-year-old Darren Watson, who lived on the landing opposite. The others, twins who lived in the block across the courtyard, seemed to be teasing him.

"Good afternoon, Darren," she said cheerfully. "And how are you today?"

"I'm fine," the little boy whispered miserably.

Something was wrong.

Anna unlocked her door and put her bags on the floor inside, listening while the older boys resumed their conversation.

"You're such a baby," said one. "Do you believe everything your mum tells you?"

"But I know he's true," said Darren uncertainly. "I've seen him."

"And you think the tooth fairy is true as well?" One of the twins poked him in the ribs. "Well, cry-baby, there's no tooth fairy, it's just your mum puts the money under your pillow. And there's no Father Christmas. It's just your dad dressed up."

"No, it isn't. My daddy's gone to heaven. But I saw Father Christmas in the shop and he said if I'm good he'll bring me just what I want."

"He's just fooling you…"

"Darren!" called Anna crisply. "I wonder if you could come and help me unpack my shopping?"

"Yes, Miss Martens." Darren scrambled up thankfully.

Continued overleaf

Continued from previous page

The boys sauntered downstairs and one of them turned and stuck his tongue out at her.

I don't know what children are coming to, thought Anna with a rush of anger.

Darren heaved up one of her bags and carried it to her kitchen triumphantly.

"I always help my Mum carry stuff," he volunteered. "But she's in bed with flu today. She can't go to work and she can't go to the shops."

"Oh, I'm sorry to hear that."

Anna believed in keeping herself to herself, and since moving into Jubilee Mansions a few months ago, had only greeted Mrs Watson briefly. The younger woman seemed friendly enough and although she appeared to be on her own, she had raised her son to be a delightful,

young and busy, always hurrying about and shouting at their children. Anna simply didn't know what to say and had never got beyond a vague smile of greeting.

"I really needed a strong pair of hands of help me with these," she continued. "Thank you, Darren. Can I pour you some orange juice? And I bought a nice ginger cake. Perhaps you'd like a slice?"

"OK!" Darren settled himself on the kitchen chair, then he blurted, "Miss, the twins were wrong, weren't they? Father Christmas is true, isn't he?"

"Father Christmas. Well now…" Anna wasn't sure how to handle this one.

"You know? The old man with a beard and a red suit? He comes the night before Christmas and he brings you a present," explained Darren confidently. "Whatever

"I was always rather scared of Black Pieter – he knew all the naughty things I'd done"

well-behaved little boy.

To her pleasure, Anna had discovered Darren had an enquiring mind and the two of them had long and serious discussions whenever they met in the courtyard. Things like why ants walked one behind the other in a line, and what shadows were and why the wind blew. Before she came to live in England, Anna had been a biology teacher in Holland and she enjoyed answering all his questions.

Darren's really the only person I've had a conversation with since I moved in here, she thought suddenly, looking down at his curly head. *It's my fault, I should make more effort.*

Yet all the other tenants seemed so

you want. My friend Henry says he comes down the chimney and puts your present in your sock, but we haven't got a chimney so I expect he'll just knock on our door."

Anna was not familiar with small boys, although she had two grown-up nephews. She tried to remember the Christmas traditions her sister had adopted when she married her English husband… there was something about writing a letter and posting it to the North Pole… She slipped easily into her teacher mode.

"Do you know, Darren, when I was a little girl in Holland, I never had a visit from Father Christmas, because he didn't come to children there. But every year we had a visit from Sinterklaas who wore long blue robes and a tall blue hat."

"Not red?"

"No, blue. Sinterklaas is what we called St Nicholas. He used to come a week or two before Christmas Day, on St Nicholas Eve and knock loudly on the front door.

"And he had a helper called Black Pieter. I was always rather scared of Black Pieter because my mother told me he knew all the naughty things I'd done during the year and he wrote them down in a very big book. And if he told Sinterklaas I hadn't been a good girl, I'd get a big black lump of coal instead of a present!"

"And did you ever? Get a lump of coal?"

Darren's eyes were round.

"No, I always received a present. I used to put my shoe out and he would leave his gift there for me to find when I woke up."

"Just like Father Christmas! He comes in the night too!"

"I remember when I was your age, he brought me something I wanted very badly, a fairy doll with a sparkly dress."

My parents must have saved every penny to buy me that, she thought affectionately, remembering how short of money they'd been after the war.

"A fairy doll?" Darren wrinkled his nose doubtfully. "Well, I really, really want a red truck. With doors that open and that little crane thing on the back that winds up."

"Oh." Anna smiled. "A tow-truck."

This didn't seem like such a difficult present to find. "Have you written and told him this?"

"Written to him? No," said Darren. "I can't write properly. Only my name. And I can write one to ten."

"Well, why don't you sit down and I'll show you how to write a letter to Father Christmas? Then you show it to your mother, and she'll post it to him."

"But how does she know where he lives?" Darren was a practical child.

"Mothers know everything," said Anna firmly. "Come on, let's find paper and a pencil. What would you like to say?"

"I don't know. I've never written a letter before. My Mum sometimes gets letters from my auntie in Canada but I don't write to her. I drew a picture for her once, though."

"Well, let's start by saying *Dear Father Christmas.*" On a second sheet, Anna wrote the words in a large firm hand. "Now, see if you can copy this."

Slowly, the tip of his tongue sticking out with the effort, Darren managed a wobbly three lines:

"Dear Father Christmas
Ples bing me a red tow trick.
Thank you love fron Darren"

"That's not bad," said Anna judiciously. "Now we'll find an envelope for this, and you take it to your mother, so she can post it. And if you're lucky, he might bring you just what you've asked him for."

Continued overleaf

"What about my mum, though?" Darren hesitated. "Can't I ask him to bring her something too? She never gets presents from anybody."

"I'm not sure if he brings things for grown ups," said Anna, amused. "What do you think she'd like?"

"She needs a coat. And some boots with warm inside. And she'd like a new cooker 'cos ours doesn't work and she wants a holiday but she says pigs will fly before she gets one." He giggled. "My Mum's funny."

"I'm pretty sure Father Christmas wouldn't have room in his sack for a cooker," said Anna. "But you could make your mother a present, as a surprise. I'm sure she'd love that."

"What sort of present?"

"How about…" Anna racked her brains, trying to remember things she'd made during the long nights in her mother's kitchen on the farm. "A paper lantern with a little candle inside? "

"Well – OK." Darren sounded dubious. "But we haven't got a candle. We switch on our lights."

"Sometimes on Christmas Eve it's fun to read a story by candlelight," said Anna, remembering how she and her sister had snuggled next to their father as he read the Christmas story by the light of an oil lamp, the snow falling outside and covering their farmyard in a thick white mantle. She couldn't remember a Christmas in Holland when it hadn't snowed. She rummaged through a drawer and found some stiff card and coloured pencils.

"You can start making it today," she said. "And I'll help you cut out pieces from the sides. Then I'll buy some glue and red Cellophane and you can finish it off here tomorrow."

She measured and cut the shape for a lantern and Darren helped her fold it along the lines she drew. His smile of satisfaction told her he was thoroughly enjoying this project.

"I won't tell my mum," he said. "It will be a secret surprise."

"Good," said Anna. "Mothers like surprises."

Well, everyone does, she thought. *Although it's been a very long time since I had a surprise, secret or not.* They were just finishing when there was a light tap on the door.

"Is Darren here, by any chance?" Mrs Watson stood on the doormat, wrapped in a blanket and looking white-faced and drawn. "Oh, there you are, Darren. I thought you were playing with the twins. Come on home now and stop bothering Miss Martens."

"No, really, he's absolutely no trouble," protested Anna. "I invited him in to give me a hand unpacking my shopping."

"And to make a secret surprise," said Darren, grinning at his mother. "But I can't tell you."

She smiled wanly, swaying on her feet.

"Thanks, Miss Martens. But we'd better get back, I'm not feeling very well."

"I can see that, my dear," said Anna, concerned. "You look as if you have a fever."

Unbidden, her hand reached out to Mrs Watson's forehead. It was burning hot.

"You go back to bed, Mrs Watson," she said. "And take some aspirin. I'll bring you a nice cup of tea."

"Please don't bother," croaked Mrs Watson. "I was just going to make one. I'll be fine. Er – my name's Emily, by the way."

"I am Anna Martens."

It felt strange, announcing her name like that. It was the first time she'd introduced herself to anyone in more than a year. When she'd come over to live near

Emily came through from her bedroom, still wrapped in her blanket.

"For us?" She whispered. "Thank you. That's very good of you, Miss Martens. It smells delicious."

Emily stayed in bed for three days and Anna helped her as much as she could. She made sure Darren got to his playgroup, did the shopping for her as well as some of her own, and tidied the flat before she fetched him at midday. Then she made him a sandwich for lunch and let him play in her flat for the afternoon to give his mother some peace and quiet.

He made a very smart lantern and she found a small candle that fitted nicely into the base.

"I haven't been well enough to brave the shops, and tomorrow is Christmas Eve"

her sister, she'd imagined she'd be absorbed into her sister's life and meet her friends.

It hadn't worked out like that because she was no sooner in her flat than her brother-in-law had been transferred to Ireland and she was left on her own, not knowing a soul.

She watched as they walked across the landing and went into their flat, Darren clutching his letter to Father Christmas.

Then she set about chopping some chicken and vegetables. Real, nourishing chicken soup, the way her mother had made it, that's what Emily Watson needed. None of this tasteless packet nonsense.

When she took it across that evening, Darren opened the door.

"Is that soup? It smells nice. Mummy!" he called happily. "Miss Martens is here."

"Mum's going to love this," he grinned, surveying his handiwork. "I still haven't told her about it. It's quite hard not to tell a secret, isn't it, Miss Martens?"

"It certainly is," she agreed.

On the fourth day, when Emily was dressed and sitting on the old sofa, she mentioned the letter to Father Christmas.

"I meant to thank you for thinking of that!" said Emily. "It was so kind of you. Darren insisted that I post it. But I haven't been well enough to brave the shops, and tomorrow's Christmas Eve."

"Ah, but I did some shopping!" said Anna. She went across the landing to her own flat and brought back an enormous red tow-truck.

Emily clapped her hand to her mouth.
Continued overleaf

"That's perfect! Exactly what he asked for! Oh, Miss Martens, you are clever!" Then she paused, looking anxious. "You must tell me how much I owe you."

"Not a penny. It will be my pleasure, just to see his face," said Anna.

"How will I ever find a sock big enough to put this gorgeous toy into?" giggled Emily, stroking the shiny red metal. "We used to put out our father's socks when I was little. But this needs a giant's sock!"

"Well, in Holland, Sinterklaas used to bang on the door on Christmas Eve. If you like, I could do that, then run back into my flat," said Anna, a gleam of mischief in her eye.

"Would you? Darren would love that!" Emily grinned. "I don't know how to repay

excited squeal at seeing the package.

"Mummy! Look, a present! For me!" Emily's voice came clearly across. "Goodness! Do you think maybe Father Christmas left it for you?"

Then Darren slammed the door shut and she heard no more. She went into her sitting room and switched on the TV, smiling in content.

Not for long. A minute later there was a knock on her door. It was Darren, his face almost split in an ecstatic grin.

"Look what I got from Father Christmas, Miss Martens!"

"Well now, isn't that wonderful? So he read your letter after all!" said Anna.

"Do you want to see how it works? I can show you with one of my other cars. Come on, Miss Martens!"

Darren obviously hadn't been able to keep his gift secret for another minute

you for everything you've done for us this past week, Miss Martens."

"I think you could start by calling me Anna," she said.

"Anna," Emily smiled.

Her name sounded so different with that strange English accent.

The following evening she waited in her flat until the time they'd agreed upon, seven o'clock. Then, with the red tow-truck wrapped in gold paper with Darren's name on it in bold black letters, she tiptoed across the landing, banged three times on Emily's front door and dashed back into her own flat, leaving it ever so slightly ajar.

She heard the door open and Darren's

He took her hand and led her across the landing.

"Darren, I don't think Mummy –"

"Ah, hello Anna!" Emily grinned at her conspiratorially. "Did you see what Darren found on our doorstep? Isn't he a lucky boy?"

"He is indeed," said Anna.

"And aren't I a lucky mum? Look what my clever son made for me!" She produced the paper lantern. "I think you might have had a hand in this!"

Darren obviously hadn't been able to keep his gift secret another minute.

"But we have a secret surprise for you, Miss Martens!" Darren was bursting, with excitement. "I made it! For you!"

"Really?" smiled Anna, taking the

clumsily wrapped little gift from him.

It was a small clay figure, painted white and sprinkled with silver glitter, with real feathers stuck into the back.

"Those are wings. That's an angel," he said, importantly. "I made it for you at play group."

"This is the most beautiful angel I have ever seen," she said truthfully. "Thank you, Darren, I shall treasure this always."

"And Mummy wrote the note," he said. "Go on, read the note."

Mystified, Anna glanced at Emily who was smiling shyly.

Dear Anna, Please would you join us for Christmas dinner at 1pm on December 25th? Love from Emily and Darren.

She swallowed, unable to speak for a second.

"Thank you, my dear, I'd love to have Christmas dinner with you," she said.

"Good! I'm so glad you haven't plans to go somewhere else," said Emily.

"No – no plans," Anna assured her. She decided to stay up late and bake some spicy ginger cookies as a contribution, the kind her mother used to make.

"I was wondering, Anna," Emily continued. "Darren said when you were little you used to read stories by candlelight on Christmas Eve."

"That's right," she agreed. "That was very long time ago."

"Well, we have the candle. And the book. So I was hoping you might feel like reading us a Christmas story?"

Anna suddenly found she had a lump in her throat.

"I could do that, yes – with pleasure," she said.

So they lit the candle in the little paper lamp, switched off the lights and Emily and Darren settled themselves on either side of Anna on the sofa.

By the flickering light, she started to read. "*A long, long time ago, in a little town called Bethlehem, a very special baby was born…*"

● ●

THE AUTHOR SAYS...

"I have a lot of friends in other countries who celebrate with different customs. Father Christmas comes in many forms but he is always a generous, jolly soul."

CODEWORD from page 19

PHRASE: TRIPLE CROWN OF ACTING

KRISS KROSS from page 47

MISSING LINK from page 101

ACROSS: 1 Sack 3 Process 9 Lasting 10 Broom 11 Issue 13 Human 14 Fret 16 Grass 18 Form 19 Laser 21 Siege 23 Stair 24 Divorce 25 Trumpet 26 Chat

DOWN: 1 Splash 2 Customer 4 Rag 5 Cable 6 Show 7 Diving 8 Smart 12 Skate 15 Research 17 Sleeve 18 Frost 20 Repeat 21 Serum 22 Fair 24 Doe

SHADED WORD: REGRET

MISSING LINK from page 141

ACROSS: 1 Rude 3 Chicken 9 Biscuit 10 Opera 11 Lemon 13 Twist 14 Used 16 Youth 18 Path 19 Owner 21 Green 23 Whale 24 Fashion 25 Present 26 Char

DOWN: 1 Rabbit 2 District 4 Hat 5 Crown 6 Even 7 Guilty 8 Faced 12 Mouse 15 Sandwich 17 Honest 18 Prawn 20 Runner 21 Guess 22 Hair 24 Fan

SHADED WORD: COUGAR

SUDOKU 1 from page 155

8	2	7	3	4	6	5	1	9
9	4	6	8	1	5	2	3	7
5	3	1	7	2	9	6	8	4
6	1	3	2	9	7	8	4	5
4	8	2	5	6	3	9	7	1
7	9	5	1	8	4	3	6	2
3	7	9	6	5	1	4	2	8
2	6	4	9	7	8	1	5	3
1	5	8	4	3	2	7	9	6

SUDOKU 2 from page 155

3	7	6	9	8	1	2	4	5
9	5	8	7	2	4	1	6	3
4	1	2	6	3	5	7	9	8
7	8	9	1	4	3	6	5	2
1	2	4	5	6	7	3	8	9
6	3	5	8	9	2	4	7	1
5	9	3	4	1	6	8	2	7
8	4	1	2	7	9	5	3	6
2	6	7	3	5	8	9	1	4

WORDWHEEL from page 155 The nine-letter word is SARTORIAL